D1598759

Toyi Elizabeth

BOOKS BY KAMRYN ADAMS

NOVELS
Par for the Curse

When the Butterfly Falls

Gathering Moss

NONFICTION

Stay in Your Lane

Fed and Focused

"My purpose in writing is to encourage you and assure you that what you are experiencing is truly part of God's grace for you. Stand firm in this grace."

1 Peter 5:12

PUBLISHER'S NOTE

In the early drafts of this novel, Toyi Elizabeth said a prayer for you at the end of each chapter. We removed the prayers from the chapters as not to disrupt the story. It was important to the author that the prayers remain in the manuscript to help guide readers on the healing journey.

For more, see the "Reader and Book Club Resources" section of this book.

AUTHOR'S NOTE

This is a fictionalized memoir.

Like all fiction, it was created from the imagination. The people in this book are characters. The events in this work may have happened to the author. They may have happened to you. Actually, they've probably happened to many of us because there's nothing new under the sun.

"History merely repeats itself. It has all been done before.
Nothing under the sun is truly new."

Ecclesiastes 1:9

PROLOGUE

Crack houses, crazy houses, and whore houses are filled with people who have similar pain to what I have experienced. Who am I? This is a question that has been asked of me my entire life. Mostly by me. Consistently by others. Here's what you need to know for now. I love Jesus and I'm not weird about it. At least, I don't think so. I pray a lot. You'll see why. I cuss a little. I'll try not to, but I can't promise you that a few bad words won't slip out along the way. I'm also a bit of a Bible nerd. I don't think I'm churchy. However, I might be a little churchy if you don't go to church.

I never finished the book, *Push*, by Sapphire. I never saw the movie it inspired starring the brilliant and beautiful Gabourey Sidibe, *Precious*. Eighteen pages into the book I called several of my girlfriends. "Tell me that this ends well. Otherwise, I'm not reading it." Not one of my girlfriends would tell me the fate of dear Precious. So I quit reading. I still don't know how it ended beyond a bunch of Oscar nominations and Mo'Nique winning the best supporting actress award for her role as the worst mother since Mommy Dearest.

I am never interested in suffering an overly emotional, heartbreaking story that doesn't offer redemption at the end. The pain and despair of others does not provide entertainment for me. I'm not one of those people who gets captivated by a fatal car crash on the side of the road. For all I know, Precious ended up having a great career, a loving family, and found healing in Jesus. That's my story. It ends well and I'm going to tell you that right up front, so you won't quit on me.

Let me assure you that what you have experienced is truly part of God's grace for you. That's what Peter tells early Christians in 1 Peter 5:12. Two-thousand years later, it's what I say to you. Your life has not been a series of coincidental mishaps. Your life is not a mistake. You didn't marry the wrong person. You did not take the wrong job. Your life story is purposeful and perfectly designed. Life is a journey without a destination. The journey is the whole point. The journey is life. When life ends, the journey ends. Not the other way around.

Some people believe that life ends when you've learned your lessons. That's not true. I know a lot of old fools who died as fools. You might believe life ends when your work is done. That's not true, either. People like MLK and JFK died in the prime of their destinies. Nobody knows the time or place that life will end. Death can happen on any day at any moment. I got tired of waiting so I took matters into my own hands.

I was cold, but not shivering. A hot, bright light shined on my face. The comforting sound of a melodious beep lulled me to sleep. Beep. Beep. Beep. Men and women draped in Carolina blue dashed back and forth around me. I heard a man say, "Stay with us young lady."

I heard the voice of a woman yell, "Help her Jesus." I could tell that it was a Black woman, not just by the rhythm in her voice but because she was calling on Jesus at work and unconcerned with who didn't like it. That's a black thing. We love our Jesus and don't care who doesn't like it. Prayer, church, and Jesus is a part of our culture. This is mostly a good thing but it also means our faith is sometimes accompanied by a "no diving" sign. Rather than developing deep faith through a relationship with Jesus rooted in The Holy Bible, we simply go to church. We relegate our faith to Sunday mornings at eleven o'clock, the most segregated hour in America. That's why many of us feel hopeless when life comes crashing down. It's why we can feel powerless to affect our futures.

It's also how I ended up in a room full of stubborn heroes who refused to accept the verdict of a slowly diminishing, euphonious beep. My fuzzy focus turned toward the doctor. I was mesmerized. He had heterochromia. One of his eyes was the color of the Caribbean ocean. The other, the color of coal. While his eyes disagreed in hue, their intentions were in full agreement. I was not going to die. In that moment, I was reminded of the arrogance of human beings. We often cannot accept the truth life gives us, so we create bite-sized versions of delusion to help us. I'm not a fan of self-deception, of any deception. I ingest heaping doses of reality daily. It's how I was raised. It's also what drove me to take a handful of a prescription drug. I won't tell you which one because I don't want you to try it.

Like I said, the story ends well. I obviously didn't die. *Thanks be to God.*

I had been procrastinating for months before it finally hit me. Singing hymns in the shower off key, I finally got the inspiration to write the story. I jumped out of the shower and raced though the master bedroom into my office leaving slushy footprints along the way. No, I didn't have the presence of mind to grab a towel first. My wrinkled hand grabbed a pen and a journal from the desk. "Ridiculously Good Ideas" was inscribed in gold lettering across the cover. A drop of water fell from my knuckle as I quickly jotted my brilliant ideas on the page.

Shivering, I ran my goosebumps back to the shower. The stream of hot water on my shoulders felt like a gentle affirming hug. Water is my thing. Oceans give me strength. Rivers help me unlock wisdom hidden within me. I took one deep, accomplished breath and— just like that, my courage was gone. It's cruel how the mind works. The right side of your brain creates amazing artistry of thought. Minutes later, the left side of your brain reveals why your idea is so glaringly stupid.

This was not a ridiculously good idea. In fact, writing a memoir is a horrible idea and I told my agent many times. Jordan insisted I write my memoirs and refused to accept any other narrative ideas from me. He said it was a good story. By "good" he meant it was entertaining and inspiring for you while dreadfully painful for me. "People love this kind of stuff," he said. In movies, it's Oscar bait. It's the stuff bestsellers are made of because the best stories come from pain. Even superhero movies are conceived out of the creator's painful sense of inadequacy. Drama, comedy, thrillers, horror, all birthed through the creator's pain. That's why writers call certain projects their "baby." It hurts like hell to birth a book.

In high school I wrote a term paper on Zora Neale Hurston. Her autobiography, *Dust Tracks on a Road*, inspired me because nobody liked it at the time that she wrote it. Critics lashed out at her for being too sympathetic to white people during a time when a strong voice of correction was needed. They say she left out big blocks of details of her life. In fact, the book mentions very little about her life as a writer.

In that book she says that there is "no greater agony than bearing an untold story inside of you." Reflecting on her words I have come to understand that the early years of my life were painful because of the things that happened to me. The balance of my pain was the burden of carrying that story inside of me. So, with the encouragement of Zora and the constant prodding from Jordan in my inbox, I finally relented to write my memoir.

As I embark upon writing "the truth," it is much more accurately defined as my truth. The villains in my story are undoubtedly heroes in their own narratives. The anti-heroes in my memories are likely superheroes in their own. This is because truth is merely a reflection of facts based on our personal experience. My sons think I'm short. My mom thinks I'm tall. All are correct from their individual experiences.

This story is being written after forgiveness, after healing, after celebration, after reflection and, yes, after that team of relentless heroes, draped in Carolina blue, saved my life. This is a purposeful, focused exposition of God's grace, favor, and faith in my life. It's more like Zora's autobiography. I'm not going to take you through a boring chronological series of events from childhood to today. I'm going to tell you stuff. Stuff I think you should know. Stuff I hope will bring restoration, reconciliation, and peace into your life.

ONE

The most important day of my life is obviously the day I was born. I entered this cruel and beautiful world at 5:55 in the morning on the 5th day of the 5th month of the year. I was born in West Virginia's 5th congressional district, which no longer exists. I am the oldest of five siblings. It has been said that I have a "five head" where most people have a forehead.

Five is my favorite number. It is the number of God's grace in the Bible. If you don't have a favorite number, it's probably because you don't have a number that defines you. Five defines me. Grace defines me. It's my story.

Born into an abundance of grace, the circumstances of my birth were chaotic. It was a peaceful, balmy spring night in Appalachia. My mother, only four months out of her teens, was sitting on her big sister's porch when she saw a shooting star dance across the sky. Apparently, it was me. A few minutes later, she was in labor. A few hours later, a terrible electrical storm ripped through the area leaving a dimly lit hospital to run on its generator. It was a storm that people talked about for a decade. It was the kind of storm that made people go to church the following Sunday.

The storm inspired my mother to name me "Stormy RaeAnn" in recognition of the extraordinary circumstances under which I was born. After the storm passed and the bright lights of the maternity wing were restored, she changed her mind. Thus, the first instance of grace in my life. *Thanks God!* I can't imagine how much more chaotic my life would have been with the name Stormy.

If you are unfamiliar with naming, let me just tell you that names matter. Sometimes God named and renamed people in the Bible to fit their personalities and destinies. Jacob, whose name meant "trickster," was a liar before he wrestled with God and become "Israel." Saul became Paul. Simon became Peter. Sarai became Sarah. An angel told Elizabeth and Zacharias to name their baby John. That was a good move because Zach the Baptist doesn't have quite the same feel.

While my mother didn't name me "Stormy," she chose a name that signals protest and battle. Consequently, I've been fighting something or someone, usually myself, since the day I was born. She chose to name me "Toyi Elizabeth."

Toyi-Toyi is the South African dance of political protest. It begins with stomping your feet. A toyi-toyi is usually accompanied by a shout of "Amandla" which means power. If you see a toyi-toyi, it is a fight for power. The name Elizabeth means "God is my oath." With a name that signals protest and a vow to God, it's no wonder my life has been... well... interesting.

My mom's name is Lacy. My dad is Judson Wilson. That's going to be important moving forward. I know my mom. I know my dad. I don't know their story. I don't remember when they were together. I have only been in the same physical space with them twice in my life, the day I was born and one terribly awkward encounter I'll tell you about later. There are no pictures of us together. No holidays. No birthday parties. There's nothing about their relationship to scare me or scar me. That might sound okay to you, but it is actually quite stressful.

Neither my mother nor my father has anything to say about their relationship. The only thing I know for sure about their life together is that they had me— which, by the way, is worth celebrating because I'm a star…apparently. I don't know how my parents met or how long they were together.

Here's what I know. There was a man who loved my mother since grammar school. He threw rocks at her bedroom window and got chased away by my grandparents. My grandmother said she saw him blaspheme the Lord when he was only "knee high to a grasshopper." She said he could lie between raindrops and out cuss a circle saw. In short, she was not a fan. When I was eight months old, my mother married this man, Bobby Sparks.

My mother and Bobby Sparks were together for sixteen years. They were often violent, terribly destructive, and the reason I spent so much time in therapy. He raised me. That was a deal between Lacy, Judson, and Bobby. I had no say in the matter. Yet, I was expected to carry the burden of this deal for most of my life.

My earliest memories are not that great. I've worked unsuccessfully with hypnotherapists and psychologists to find "better" memories, but they don't exist. A few doctors with "revolutionary" techniques have tried to uncover the better memories hidden below the pain. What we've discovered is that there is nothing in that dried up well. There are no better memories that I'm suppressing. I've created some great memories since then. I've had some serious wins and lots of laughter in my life, but when it comes to the early years…it is what it is. They suck.

This is my earliest memory…

It was a chilly fall night. I sat high upon Bobby Spark's shoulders with my toddler hands clutching his ears. My pink pajama feet hung over his shoulders as I watched our family home burn to the ground. I can still recall the blazing heat on my face. The flames danced violently in my eyes. The heat on my face was oddly comforting. I don't remember being scared. I don't recall being rushed from the house in terror. Honestly, I don't even remember living in that house. I only remember sitting high above the ground, mesmerized by the heat and bright light of the fire. I was only two years old, but

I remember those flames and how they felt on my face. That's my earliest memory— a house in flames.

My next earliest memory is not so fuzzy. In fact, it is painfully clear and still ranks as one of the worst memories of my life— and that's saying a lot. I was three years old. I know because my little brother was just an infant swaddled in his crib. I sat in the dark at the top of a steep staircase and watched Bobby battle my mother in a rage that only the United States Marine Corps can create. She screamed. He barked. An invisible Oorah! crashed against the walls of our home. Bobby dragged my mother back and forth across my line of sight. He punched, slapped, and kicked her. Then he spit in her face.

I ran back to my brother's crib and got up on my tippy toes to peak at him. He was still asleep. I smiled through the tears and stretched my little arm through the rail. I couldn't reach his back. In my mind I was big enough to comfort him, but my arms were too short and frail. That's still who I am today. I think I can do anything. I don't care how short and frail I may appear. I'm a giant in my mind.

Not unlike any other big sister, I felt a surge of responsibility and honor the day my little brother came home from the hospital. It was my job to protect him from the chaos of our home. So, I ran back to the top of the stairs. I screamed at my parents with tears burning down my face.

I shrieked, "STOP! You're going to wake up the baby!" I screamed over and over again. "Stop! Stop it, Daddy! Stop it!" I yelled so loud and cried for so long that I eventually puked on my bare feet. I screamed and puked some more.

The sound of my retching apparently ripped Bobby from his imaginary battle with the Viet Cong. He and my mother dashed up the stairs, racing towards me together as a team. Bobby scooped me out of my vomit and into his arms. My mother forced a smile from her swollen, tear-stained faced. I sobbed.

"It's okay. We're okay," Bobby reassured me.

They carried me into my bedroom. I loved that room. It was everything a little girl could want. Pink and frilly with ruffles and too many dolls for two hands to enjoy. The walls were papered with butterflies. Mama and Bobby Sparks laid me gently under the canopy of the full-size bed I had just gotten as a "big sister" gift. Then, they sang me a song.

"I love little Toyi Sparks. Swinging in the trees... eating all the apples."

They tickled me and smothered me in kisses on both cheeks and my belly. We laughed. I giggled until my tears of terror were replaced with happy tears. I had done it. I had figured out how to tame the monster and the baby was still asleep. From that moment, I inserted myself into every raging, violent episode between mama and Bobby Sparks. I was so effective at taming Uncle Sam's monster that my mother became dependent on my intrusion.

"Toyi, help!" She'd call out to me while trapped in a corner with Bobby looming over her. "Help me!"

I'd pull at his legs and jump on his back until he came to himself.

I was always so involved in their relationship and they often made it about me. He married her because I needed a dad. She married him for the same reason. Basically, everything was all my fault. That's how it felt for a long time.

Each of them complained to me about the other. They told me things no child should know about their parents. The goal was to turn me against the other one. They had me keep the secrets of their adulterous shenanigans and involved me in their disputes. They were like two siblings who bickered constantly because they hated each other. It was awful.

Period. By the time I was fourteen I felt like the only adult in the house.

That's it. Those are the earliest memories of my life. I've been told many stories about my toddler years. They say I was silly, always laughing, dancing, and putting on a show. They say I was the happiest baby on the block. I don't remember that. I only remember being terrified, scared, and insecure. I only recall being a problem solver, trying to get out of the day's mess. I listen to fond memories about my adolescence and wonder who the heck people are talking about. They say I was always kind. I remember being angry. They say I was always smiling. I remember being suicidal in excruciating emotional pain until I was almost thirty years old.

Accepting these circumstances have helped me navigate my life. I came into the world during a historic storm. I was born with nurses and doctors frantically running around the hospital in darkness. I'm not comfortable with easy assignments. I'm sure they're nice, but I would not know where to begin. I work with broken, messy stuff. It's all I know. God bless the people who were given fully intact lives and simply told, "Don't mess it up." I was given a broken life and told to "make it happen."

My story is convoluted with fabrications and fables. It took years to uncover and discover my true identity. Do you recall the song I told you my parents sang to me? Little Toyi Sparks? Sparks is Bobby's last name. It's my brother's last name. It was not my name. It wasn't even my mom's last name for very long.

As it turns out, Bobby and my mom divorced a couple of years into their marriage and never remarried. Fourteen of the sixteen-year reign of terror was completely unbinding and totally voluntary. She just signed us up for that mess. She could have freely walked away any day. Eventually she did. We'll get to that part a little later.

When I was four years old, I learned my real name. I had the same last name as my father, but I matriculated through primary and secondary school with a fake birth certificate that listed me as "Toyi Sparks." It's what everybody called me. Some people still do and I cringe every time I hear it.

On my sixteenth birthday, I signed my real name for the first time, Toyi Elizabeth Wilson. Thank God that a driver's license is an official, legal document that required my social security number. The jig was up, but at that point everybody knew and loved me as Toyi Sparks. It was impossible and quite embarrassing to change my name at that point. So, I decided to hide my driver's license from my friends until things settled down. While everyone else ran into school shouting about their new rite of passage, I allowed people to think I had failed my driver's test. Once the initial excitement of my friends waned, nobody ever asked to see my license. We were all drivers. That's what mattered.

I tried to apply to colleges with my birth name but "Toyi Wilson" had no academic records and no explanation for the name change. It was too complicated to navigate. So, I arrived on campus as Toyi Sparks with a driver's license that read Toyi Wilson. It got even more complicated as life progressed. Shortly after I got everything changed over to my birth name, I got married. Then, I got divorced and went back to my maiden name. Then I married again. I've had five different name changes in my life. Six, if you count the hour I was named Stormy RaeAnn.

If you've changed your mind and you don't want to take this journey with me, then remember one thing.

Accepting your story is the very first step in building a powerful, authentic, dope ass life. Trust that every day of your life was designed to make you exactly who you are. Your backstory is what it is. You can't change it. You can, however, change the trajectory of the rest of your life. It might not be easy, but it's possible.

TWO

Though I had five grandparents, I was closest to my mother's parents. My maternal grandmother, Emmy Lou, was the love of my life. We called her "Nang." She was tall and broad with strong hands and gentle eyes. She looked like Lena Horne in the face but was built to dunk on somebody. My grandfather, "Grandpa Sam" easily weighed a hundred pounds less than she did. She called him "two peas on a board" because that's what he looked like from the side— two peas glued to a popsicle stick.

Nang and I had our thing. It was eating. She baked the smoothest, fluffy delicious lemon meringue pies the world had ever known. She did not fill her pies with that yellow, translucent jelly you find in hospital cafeterias and roadside diners. Nang made her lemon pie filling with pudding and evaporated milk. Nang's lemon meringue pie easily ranks as one of the happiest memories of my childhood.

While the pie was still warm, Nang would slice it right down the middle. Half for her. Half for me. We sat on the porch with our individual hunks of lemon heaven. Nang and I talked about everything while warm pudding pie soothed our palates. She told me how smart I was. She told me that beauty on the inside glows on the outside. She told me that I should "pick shit with chickens" before I let anyone manipulate me for the sake of material gain. She often asked me what was going on at home with Mama and Bobby. Like most Black children, I was raised not to tell our family business.

"How is your mama fairing with that rascal?" she asked.

I quickly shoveled pie into my mouth to avoid answering.

"I won't say anything," she assured me.

I fell for that line too many times to count. Each time I got in big trouble at home.

The hardiest laughter of my childhood happened at Nang's and Grandpa Sam's house. When I was sixteen, I went to live with them. I slept on the "good sofa" in the living room. My cousin, who also lived with them, had the second bedroom. For years Nang didn't allow anyone to sit on her living room furniture. When I needed a place to sleep, she didn't give a damn about that couch. The off-limits living room became my bedroom, and my personal items cluttered her favorite space. She gave up the most sacred place in her home to make space for me.

Nang and I got along very well. When she disciplined me, I knew she was right. She once slapped the piss out of me... literally... for having a hickey on my neck. I've never had one since. She corrected me using a thin, wispy switch from a weeping willow in the back yard. I had no idea that "weeping" was the real name of the tree until I was older. I assumed she had given the tree that name for an obvious reason. It made us cry. Nang disciplined me with a loving heart and a firm hand. No pun intended.

Nang managed to get me off to college. She did her part by praying and asking me about my process. I did my part by securing a full engineering scholarship. Granted, I didn't want to be an engineer. For the time being, I just needed to get to college. I planned to work out the minor detail of how to pay for it later. Worse case scenario, I would become an engineer and make enough money to go back and study whatever I wanted.

That was a stupid plan, but it worked. I earned a full university scholarship and changed my major to Chemistry/Pre-Pharmacy. It took some maneuvering and manipulating but I did it. I was proud of myself, but Nang was even more proud of me.

One busy Friday when I was in college, Nang called and asked me to come home for the weekend.

"I have things to do," I said.

Nang refused to take "no" for an answer and our discussion turned to conflict. I asserted myself in a completely inappropriate tone and volume. When I was twelve, I saw Nang slap my mother for raising her voice. She was thirty-three years old at the time. I remember thinking, "I'm never going to be grown."

Without a doubt, Nang would have slapped me had we been in the same room. Lucky for me, she was nearly two hundred miles away. This was our first disagreement. I was adamant that I needed to stay focused on my schoolwork and family priorities. She was insistent that I come home for the weekend. I refused and argued my points.

"Well, when are you coming home?" she asked.

"Soon. I promise," I said. And I meant it.

"Soon…"

Her voice trailed off and it rang funny in my ears. There was an awkward pause before we said a disappointing goodbye and hung up the phone. She was disappointed that I wasn't coming home. I was disappointed that she didn't recognize my new adulthood or my responsibilities as a young wife, mother, and full-time student. I wasn't a kid anymore. I couldn't just run home for the weekend.

Terribly upset, I spent the weekend studying as best I could. My son, Caden, who was younger than two at the time, was completely unaware of his stake in my academic success. Caden wanted to watch Aladdin and he wanted to watch it with me. So, we watched Aladdin. Then we watched it again. And again. When Caden went to bed, I pulled an all-nighter making flashcards and highlighting seventy percent of the words on every page.

I was prepared but I was exhausted. At one point during the exam, I thought I saw Caden run by the classroom door. Like I said, I was exhausted. It was hard to focus on the test because I kept thinking about my argument with

Nang. I was sleep deprived, anxious, and very upset. I replayed over and over the way she said, "soon." She was defeated and disappointed. It echoed in my ears like a haunting taunt.

After the exam, I trudged across campus like a zombie. When I arrived at my car, I threw my sorority book bag in the backseat. Hungry for sleep, I shifted into drive and pulled the car forward. That's when Caden appeared in front of me. It turns out I wasn't seeing things after all.

This is a good time to introduce you to Marcos Gamble. Mocha and masculine, he was everybody's All-American. The shining star on a dimly capable team, Marcos was projected to go first in the NFL draft to the Cleveland Browns. He had already been on the cover of SI twice. Like Rick Fox and Matt Leinart, people rooted for him because he was handsome. One sports column dubbed him "rookie most likely to date Halle Berry." That would have been cute except that he was already married to me.

Marcos grew up in Chicago, but his grandmother was from Galia City, my hometown in Appalachia. It's where he spent his summers. Every summer, teenage girls in Galia and the surrounding county were boy-crazy for one boy, Marcos

Gamble. I was never interested in Marcos for two reasons. One, I already had a boyfriend. Two, I almost failed kindergarten for not knowing how to share. Ironically, these are also the reasons we divorced.

Back to the story…

Marcos scooped Caden in his arms and walked to the driver's side. I rolled down the window, happy to see them. "What are you guys doing here?"

I kept my foot on the brake, but never put the car in park. I should have put the car in park.

"Come on, we're going to Galia City," he said.

"Are you serious?" I asked.

With a nod, his lips quivered into a smile and tears welled in his eyes. He dislodged the words from his throat. "Nang died."

I punched open the car door and dashed across the parking lot. I don't know why I ran or where I was going. Marcos jumped inside the car and slammed the gear to park. Then, he sprinted in my direction. I'm pretty sure he ran faster on this day than he did at the combine. He grabbed me from behind and smothered me in his chest. I flailed and flopped like a rag doll while Marcos held me up.

A campus police officer stopped and got out of the car, "Are you okay, Marcos?"

"Yes, this one is my wife," he said. Marcos shooed the officer away. "You can go."

Obviously, I didn't catch it at the time. It would be weeks before I processed his words. After everything I had been through, God owed me better than this. It was my time. I was a wife and a mother. I was building the perfect life I always wanted with the perfect guy (or so I thought at the time) and the perfect kid (still totally think this). Loss was not supposed to happen to me anymore. It was over. I had paid my dues. My children were supposed to know Nang and love her lemon meringue pie. This was not the way it was supposed to go.

Grandpa Sam died four months later. Those four months were a whirlwind. I remember calling every day and going back to Galia City several times. I remember having the neighbors check on him and talking with doctors as his kidneys failed. I can recall so many details about Grandpa Sam's funeral, but Nang's funeral is a complete blur except for two things: standing over her casket and the dress I wore.

At the funeral, I wore an emerald green dress that hit midway between my ankles and kneecaps. It hugged every curve and swerve of my twenty-three-year-old body. I was grown now. I had a flat stomach and childbirth hips. People kept telling me how great I looked. I boiled in anger with every mention of that dress.

"Girl, you are wearing that dress."

"That dress is saying something."

"Girl, let me get that dress."

I would have given that dress to anyone who could bring Nang back to me. Stupid dress!

My family was very focused on my pain during the time of Nang's death. There was a collective awareness of my guilt that was too awkward to speak of. I stood over the casket for a very long time. So long that it made the other mourners uncomfortable. So long that I don't remember anything else about the funeral. I stood over the casket staring down at the love of my life until Grandpa Sam approached and grabbed my arm. "You been up here long enough, gal. Let's go."

He pulled me away and I resisted. He took two steps and decided to address the invisible gorilla in the room. "She knew you loved her."

I lost it. I think I cried for three days. I'm not sure.

A week after we buried Nang I sat on the sofa and watched Caden play with a newspaper. He had a room full of toys, but kids prefer to play with things like wrapping paper to punctuate the foolishness of their parents who spend too much money on toys. He said, "Mommy, are you sad?"

"No, I'm just thinking."

Indeed, I was thinking. I was sad, too. I racked my brain on how to bring my grandmother back from the grave. It was the oddest feeling. It was, by far, the most important day in the development of my character.

Until then, I was smart enough, pretty enough, charismatic enough, or simply resolved enough to change any situation, to solve any problem. I was the little girl who knew how to stop Bobby from beating my mother. I was the teenager who found an engineering scholarship to go to college and then earned another scholarship to study what I wanted. I was the woman who went to summer school while I was pregnant, had a baby, sat out in the fall, and returned to school right on schedule. I made things happen. Nothing was out of my control or immune to my influence. That's who I was…until Nang died.

In a stupor, I gazed around the apartment to discern what was happening. The TV was on. Marcos was at his summer "job," which was code for collecting a check without violating NCAA policy. My mom was estranged. I hadn't seen my dad in fifteen years. My little brother was doing well. My grades were good. My future was bright. My grandmother was dead. That's what was happening.

Nang taught me to "see things for what they are, not what you want them to be." She taught me to pay my bills in full because "if you can't pay ten you certainly can't pay twenty." Nang taught me that once you learn something nobody can take it away from you. While my grandmother taught me many things while she was alive, she taught me the most important lesson with her death. There is a God, and He is the one in control.

I was not pretty enough, smart enough, or influential enough to bring my grandmother back. I could not manipulate God to do what I wanted him to do. It was real and it was irreversible. It was one the most important days of my life and it broke me. In the aftermath of Nang's death, I came to realize that some things are permanent. Some things are painful. When faced with something permanent and painful, we have but one choice that matters... acceptance.

Ignoring truth doesn't erase it. Creating a narrative to cover truth, doesn't revise it. You can't out-hustle God. You can't fake out God. You cannot lie, smile, or talk your way through life. You can't buy bigger houses, boats, and more red bottoms to fill the hole in your heart. You will eventually have to accept the truth. God is in control. He sees you. He knows you. He loves you anyway.

I want to leave you with this last thing. It's important. Not going to see my grandmother that weekend was a mistake. It was my mistake. I promised myself that I would never make that kind of mistake again. I don't let the day end in conflict. I don't let the sun go down on my anger. I say, "I'm sorry," just in case today is my last opportunity to do so. If you need to apologize to someone, I pray that you do it today. It might be your last opportunity to do so.

THREE

Marcos only beat me once. The other three hundred times, we fought. In my mind, there was a difference between being a battered wife and a fighting wife. Marcos was not a wife-beater. That term conjures visions of cowering women in corners being thrashed by men in sleeveless white tees who spew bourbon breath onto their fragile wives. I was nobody's fragile wife. Perhaps, that was the problem.

In hindsight, I could have diminished much of the chaos by bowing out and removing myself from the situation. Maybe if I didn't fight back, the episodes would have ended quicker and without injury. That was not my way of doing things. After watching Mama be beaten by Bobby Sparks, I refused to take my lumps without a fight. We were young and under pressure. Frustration was the air we breathed so we fought. I never won a fight. That didn't matter to me.

In these fights I was a wild woman, kicking, clawing, biting, and inflicting any amount of pain in my strength. I was only one hundred, eleven pounds back then, but I could pack a punch with a bit of a sting. Once, my punch connected in just the right part of Marcos' jaw. It stunned him. Marcos dragged me into the bedroom and slammed me onto the bed. He mashed my face into the mattress until I got lightheaded and we both assumed it would be my last breath. Then, he let me go.

"Calm down! I'm sorry. Okay?" His apology was supposed to undo everything.

As soon as I caught my breath, I'd take another swing at him. "Keep your hands off of me."

This outburst caused Marcos to form tackle me with all of his weight. My body crashed to the floor and it felt like my bones shattered like a glass vase, the kind that he was sure to bring full of flowers later. Unable to recover from the blow, I accepted my defeat. Until next time.

Marcos and I didn't physically fight every day or even every week. Fear and intimidation were more his thing.

Marcos' ex-girlfriend had warned me, but I thought she was just jealous. She told me a story about how he once hung over the railing of a cruise ship and threatened to throw her in the ocean. I thought that was preposterous until the day he sprayed me with lighter fluid and chased me through the house threatening to set me on fire. Deep down I knew he didn't want to kill me. But I was petrified that one day he'd kill me by accident.

I wasn't much of a physical match for Marcos. Though emotionally, I could do a lot damage. I was like a mosquito, tiny and seemingly inconsequential until I bite you. The sensation of my bite stays with you for a long time... even if you kill me. If you don't kill me— and that would be your mistake, the bite only serves to nourish my future conquests. This is why I don't consider myself to be a queen bee. A honeybee dies when it stings you. I am a queen mosquito. The more I bite, the stronger I get.

Crazy was my superpower back then and I knew how to use it. I'd throw dishes of pasta against the wall, cut up Marcos' clothes and leave them in a pile outside the door. I'd throw drinking glasses from the terrace as he pulled away from home. I wasn't able to do much to his strong body, but boy could I wound his ego. It was the weakest, most fragile part of him.

One time I kicked in the locker room door after finding a bottle of doxycycline hidden in the closet. He had chlamydia and I made sure everybody knew it. When he fractured my jaw, I went straight to the offensive coordinator's house with my purple swollen face. He took me to the university ER quietly, without incident or press attention. The coaching staff feared that I would make his true nature public. If so, his good church boy image would be shattered. The league didn't need another angry Negro, they needed Marcos. That was the Big Joker I held in my back pocket. Don't forget, we all wanted to be like Mike before we knew who he really was.

At the climax of our demise, Marcos knocked me unconscious with a telephone— a solid, heavy 1990's Bell South telephone, not one of these lightweight computer cameras we use today. A real phone. He snatched it from the wall and wrapped the cord around my neck. I fought to get away.

"I hate you!" I screamed.

He hit me right across the face and knocked me out cold.

In the moment, I'm sure Marcos thought I was dead. Honestly, so did I. By the grace of God, I woke up and opened my eyes. The room didn't spin. It glitched like a scrambled television. Hundreds of twinkling bright spots filled my view. In the midst of them was one frightened little boy in the big body of a first-round draft pick. I was concussed and Marcos knew it. I had a severe, grade-three concussion, out for five minutes and eighteen seconds. I want you to sit in silence for five minutes and eighteen seconds. That's a long time to believe you killed someone.

Marcos lifted me from the floor and placed me gently on the same bed that he often used as a weapon to suffocate me. I had no fight left. A sharp pain dashed across my face and into the top of my head at the sound of Marcos' pager. I shrieked in horror because it electrified my bones like a lightning strike. This was the day I had been afraid of. The day when Marcos would accidentally kill me while simply trying to control me.

Finally, I opened my mouth to speak. "Where did you learn this?" I desperately needed to reconcile the moment.

Marcos remained quiet. The whites of his eyes turned pink like he had developed a sudden case of conjunctivitis. He clenched his jaw tight enough to break a tooth. I could see the decision blitzing through his mind. To tell the truth or not. We locked eyes. I waited for an answer.

"Where do you think?" he said and fell into my lap. His sobs frightened me. I had never seen him so vulnerable and afraid. So...human.

I held that answer in my heart for many years. It has helped me to forgive Marcos over and over...and over again. How could I have been so blind? In my own brokenness I never considered his childhood pain. Because my family was so fractured, I never saw the misery and dysfunction of his family until that moment. I didn't realize it at the time, but Marcos' constant reminder that nobody loved me was in response to his own insecurity. His abusive treatment of me and his unyielding control of my life was actually his fear of not being loved by me. He felt ashamed about who he was and how he came to be. His backstory was almost as convoluted as mine. He had lived in the dark places of his parents' relationship, not unlike me. Marcos was just as broken as me, arguably more so. We both needed Jesus. I found Him one crisp autumn day in October.

It was a good day. All was well. The sun was taking its final bow across the sky when, suddenly, the sky darkened. It was as if the sun decided to end its dance in a frenzied exit. The world went gray and snow fell from the clouds quicker than either of us could process it.

Snow in October in the Northeast is not welcome, but not at all a surprise. It is, however, a phenomenon in the autumn months of the South. The big, fluffy snowflakes quickly turned to a "wintry mix" which is rain, freezing rain, sleet, and snow mixed together into a dangerous cocktail. It was shocking, most surreal. The zooming, open-road traffic on the highway had come to a crawl. Visibility was minimal except for a line of cars that lit up the roadside with flashing hazard lights. Our rear-wheel-drive sports car was not made for this kind of weather. The tires spun, we slid to the side and then it happened…

Our car turned 180 degrees, facing oncoming traffic. Only a few feet behind us, a semi truck managed to shift lanes like it was a fiat. Marcos could not get the car turned around in the right direction. The wheels spun with a grinding sound against the ice. Marcos flashed the high beams to warn the oncoming traffic. My heart thumped. Sweat dripped from his temple as we hoped cars would see us in enough time to change lanes without sliding into us. He was afraid so I became afraid, too. I prayed. The wheels finally got some traction and Marcos was able to turn the car.

Our silence spoke of our fear and a terrible truth plagued me. I felt its infection growing in my body.

"Marky..." I said with a question in my tone.

"Yeah," he answered with the same uncertainty.

"If we had died, I'm not sure I would go to heaven," I said.

Marcos assured me with a comforting chuckle. "If you don't go, nobody's going."

An incredible emptiness filled me. It was a gaping, invisible, dark void. I loved church. I loved hymns. I loved reading my Bible before I went to bed. I taught Sunday School and VBS. I had been in all the Christmas plays and memorized all the verses. All of this was true, but there was a hole in my heart where Jesus should have lived. When faced with death, I was plagued with the shocking reality that despite doing all the "stuff," I didn't really know Jesus.

Otherwise, I wouldn't have been so uncertain about my afterlife.

Like Saul on the way to Damascus, this was my moment. I'm telling you... It was physically impossible for that semi-truck not to crush us. It was too close behind us. It was too big to change lanes so quickly. We should be dead. God spared our lives.

I bowed my head in prayer and closed with, "Thank you Jesus."

While I was praying, the snow stopped. The sun returned to finish its bow as if the frightening intermission never happened. There was no question. That storm was so odd, so powerful, so brief that I knew God wanted my attention. Even Marcos, who wasn't impressed by anything but his stats and his own reflection, marveled at the sight. "Look at that sun," he said.

I looked up and I saw Jesus for the first time. No, I didn't see the guy with the blond hair in all the portraits. I also didn't see Black Jesus that looks like Ned the wino. I didn't see a person at all. I simply saw the sun in all of its magnificence. Everything changed.

As a teenager, I struggled to understand God and why he let so many terrible things happen in my life. I concluded that God didn't love me. I thought God made victors and victims and I was relegated to being the latter. I didn't really know God. I viewed God as the great "Thou Shalt Not" who entertained himself by zapping us when we do things wrong. God was mean and unfair to me. God allowed me to be abused, abandoned, and objectified. I spent my life trying to earn God's love and change his opinion of me. I wanted to show him that I deserved to be loved. On this day, I thought I had finally earned it.

In my view, God saved my life that day. It was the first time that "the worst thing that could happen" didn't actually happen to me. It changed everything. I had worked my whole life to get God's attention. I did everything "right" so that God would love me. I did all the "stuff" and was known for being a Christian. After that day, reading the Bible was a completely different experience for me. Where I usually skipped over Matthew 1 and all those "begats" I now saw redemption. Rahab, Bathsheba, raggedy Judah, and lying ass Jacob were used to bring forth the Messiah.

The more I read, the more I loved Jesus and the better I got to know God. I had not earned God's love that day on the road. It wasn't the first day he paid attention to me. God's grace had been with me from the beginning. I didn't need to earn it. Such is the definition of grace. All I had to do was look up and see that Jesus was with me. All that was required of me to get God's love and approval was to simply open my heart to receive it.

Grace. God's grace represented by the number five. I had been born into grace and under grace. Grace is so easily obtained. Yet, so difficult to grasp. Once I realized that God loved me, I began the healing journey to where I am today. I'm not "there" yet and I have much more growing and learning to do. However, I am a completely different person from the broken girl that kicked in the locker room doors and banged on side-chick windows demanding that my husband come outside.

After the day I saw Jesus in the sun everything changed. It didn't change overnight. Later that year, I was diagnosed with a chronic illness and had major surgery that removed half of my lung. Marcos was still cheating, and I secured my own "entanglement"to bite him. This time, I didn't blame

God for any of it. This time, I didn't think it was because God hated me. From the day I saw Jesus in the sun, I understood that bad things happened for one reason... because life happens. The only thing I knew at that point was that God loved me and that my life would not always be so chaotic. So... I took one step at a time.

Giving your life to Christ doesn't make life perfect. It doesn't necessarily make it easy, either. It just makes the difficulties of life easier to handle by keeping the faith. Faith gives you hope and peace. In the book of John, Jesus tells his disciples who he is. He also tells them who they are because of Him. Then, he tells them one really important thing. It's something Jesus wanted them to know. It's something I want you to know. In John 16:33, Jesus tells the disciples, "In this world, you will have troubles. But take heart! I have overcome the world."

I was born in a spring lightning storm. I was born again in an autumn snowstorm. My life has been filled with storms— physical, emotional, and spiritual. Even without the name "Stormy" my life was tumultuous, chaotic, and full of calamity. If it wasn't, you wouldn't be reading this book right now. Thanks be to God.

You are not the only child who was abandoned. You are not the only woman being cheated on. You are not the only man who made mistakes in your marriage. You are not alone in falling and failing to live out your faith with integrity. God is with you. His grace is sufficient, and his power is perfect in our weakness. Life is full of trouble. It gets hard. For everybody, not just you. So get over yourself and keep the faith, baby.

FOUR

We've already established that I needed a huge dose of faith from the day I was born. Faith helps you make sense of things. Faith is the older, smarter, stronger version of hope. My faith has been forming since I was a child. Yours has too. When you were born, how you were born, and to whom you were born are all necessary elements to develop your faith. Many people have a hard time connecting to God, the Heavenly Father, because of the relationship they have with their dads. I'm no different. A large part of my faith developed through my relationship with my dad.

When I was a little girl, I spent alternate weekends with my paternal grandparents, The Wilsons. My Grandpa Ted gave me animal cookies and ice cream before dinner. My Grandma Melanie spun me around in new dresses and sang songs about how pretty I was... and smart. They made sure I knew that I was special. Before I left their home on Sunday evenings, my grandmother would hug me tight and remind me, "You're the star God sent from Heaven."

Their presence in my life made me aware that there was another side of me. Even though I didn't know my dad, I knew I had one because I had grandparents. They told me stories about this invisible man, Judson, who loved me very much.

Like all little girls, my daddy was a superhero in my mind. He was the biggest brightest, most handsome, smartest, most perfect figment of my imagination. At that time, he was the benchmark for everything I wanted to be. He left Appalachia and so could I. He lived in a big city far away and so would I. In my mind, Daddy was perfect. Then one day I heard my grandfather blame Grandma Melanie for spoiling my dad. Their voices were raised, but not like at my house. It was a normal volley of words; the kind most married people have after years of being together.

As a little girl, I was very good at being not seen and not heard. Back then I was keenly aware to stay in a child's place. I had an uncanny ability to make myself invisible like a wall portrait that just hangs around year after year. I could quietly slide into a room of adults and listen for a few minutes before anyone noticed I was there. I heard everything. I just knew better than to comment on it.

"That's why he won't do right by this child," Grandpa Ted said.

Then, Grandma Melanie blamed Mama. "That girl..." Thereby proving my grandfather's point.

I sauntered into the kitchen without them seeing me.

"Judson's no good," Grandpa Ted said. Then, he looked down and saw me. With a heavy apology in his eyes, he grabbed my hand. "Your daddy loves you, but he's trifling."

I didn't know what trifling meant but I could tell by Grandpa Ted's tone and Grandma Melanie's face that it didn't mean "perfect." I was pretty certain it wasn't something celebratory. Grandma Melanie reinforced the point that Daddy loved me. Their conversation had killed my perfect superhero. From then on Daddy would be my trifling superhero, but a superhero, nonetheless.

My childhood was a lot of things, chaotic, dysfunctional, and unhealthy. However, the most consistent description of my childhood would be the word, "stressful." It was stressful because I had so many secrets to keep. The adults in my life, even those who meant to nurture me, buried me under their secrets and held my truth hostage.

Grandpa Ted and Grandma Melanie were a big secret I had to keep as a little girl. Along with my mother, my grandparents…all four of them… devised a visitation plan without Bobby Sparks knowing. My mom dropped me off at Nang's house on Fridays. Then, about a half-hour later, Grandpa Ted picked me up for the weekend. He and Grandma Melanie lived about fifteen miles up the road where I would stay until Sunday evening after dinner. It was a secret. I wasn't allowed to tell anybody that I visited with my grandparents.

Because my mother has always been a bit passive aggressive, she leaked the secret during one of her battles with Bobby Sparks. There was cussing, fussing, and blaspheming the name of the Lord. Once Bobby found out about the visits, I was forbidden to see my paternal grandparents ever again. They sent me checks that he didn't cash. They wrote me letters he didn't let me read.

A short time later Grandma Melanie died. Nobody took me to the funeral. I was told I wasn't invited. I was pretty sure you didn't need to be invited to a funeral, but I just went with it at the time. I had a mini funeral for Grandma Melanie at my Barbie dream house. I cried and said goodbye. Afterwards, I felt better.

When Grandma Melanie died, my Grandpa Ted went to live with my dad and I never saw him again. I also never forgot what he told me. "Your daddy loves you, but he's trifling."

It's ironic that as "trifling" as my father was, nobody had anything bad to say about him. In nearly fifty years, the only person I've ever heard say anything negative about my dad was my Grandpa Ted. To everybody else, including the little girl inside me, he's a superhero…a perfect one who can leap tall buildings in a single bound and outrun a locomotive.

Your parents are the two most important people in your life, both of them. You can disagree with me if you like, but without those two people you would not be here. You would not be who you are. God chose your parents, both of them, with capital "p" Perfection.

God created you, and your parents were responsible for the day-to-day upkeep. Think of yourself as a car. God is the manufacturer. Your parents are the owners. They may have been neglectful owners who left you sitting on the street with an oil leak and four flat tires. Perhaps you lucked out and got exceptional owners who washed and shined you every week and filled you with premium fuel so you could be the best version of you. Most people got regular ol' owners who washed them when they got dirty, changed the oil when necessary, and sprung for premium fuel when they had the resources to do so.

By the time we reach adulthood most of us know that our parents aren't perfect. Their childhoods weren't perfect. Their marriage wasn't perfect. Their choices weren't perfect. Our parents are flawed human beings like us. If you're over the age of thirty and still think your parents are perfect, one day you are going to discover that they've been lying to you for your entire life. They have big secrets. Start saving for therapy now.

I am grateful that I didn't carry the innocent privilege of thinking my parents were perfect. Like I said, I was about six when I found out my dad was trifling. I pretty much knew my mom was trifling even though I still wasn't completely clear on the definition. After nearly fifty years of being a daughter and a mother for over half of those years, I've come to believe one very important thing about all parents... No parent intends to screw up their kid.

My parents made some really bad decisions. Those decisions were made in my best interest. Believe it or not, a mother who leaves her newborn baby in a dumpster believes she is doing what's best for her child. In her mind, the child is not going to spend eighteen years in foster care being abused and mistreated. In that mother's mind, the baby will be given to a loving family with plenty of resources. She imagines that the baby will take vacations to Disneyland and earn a law degree from Yale before going on to become the President of the United States of America.

When I was a baby, my dad wrote a letter to Bobby Sparks. This letter remains in the Bobby Sparks archives of justice and justification. The letter says something like this...

"Dear Bobby, as far as I am concerned you are Toyi's father. I will not interfere. I do not want to be a part of her life. You can have her. Take her. She's yours."

I'm pretty sure my dad wasn't signing me up to become a terrified, abused little girl. He didn't expect me to become a traumatized teenager drowning in fear and shame. When my dad wrote that letter to Bobby Sparks, I'm absolutely positive he didn't think the first twenty-five years of my life would end up being what they were. He had loving and supportive parents and I'm sure he thought I'd get the same. He was wrong.

My mom chose to stay with Bobby Sparks for almost seventeen years. Despite staying with Bobby, she never allowed him to formally adopt me. Before I went to kindergarten, Mama and Bobby Sparks sat me down and told me that I was Daddy's daughter, but I was going to school with Bobby Sparks' last name. It might sound crazy now, but it made perfect sense to a five-year-old. They taped the name "Toyi Elizabeth Sparks" over top of "Toyi Elizabeth Wilson" on my birth certificate. They taped a piece of paper with "Bobby Sparks" over top of "Judson Wilson" and made a Xerox copy to enroll me in school. My identity was stolen long before the internet was created.

Mama and Bobby were forced to tell me the truth because we were going back to West Virginia and everybody in Galia City knew that Judson Wilson was my father. In small towns, if you don't know something it is simply because you don't know. It is not because it's a secret. There are no secrets in small town America. Everybody knows everything if anybody knows it.

Mama and Bobby were worried that some mean-spirited kid with gossipy parents would break the news to me and break my heart in the process. It was the right decision because that's exactly what happened at my Aunt Gloria's annual July 4th cookout.

It was the Sparks family reunion. We returned from California every year, never to miss it. It was the kind of event were every adult was an "uncle" or "auntie" and every child was a "cousin." Most of them were not actually related, but it's the way we do things in our culture.

An adult was only "Mister" or "Miss" if they weren't close to your family. In fact, I once called a man "Mister Jeffrey" and it offended him. I had to apologize and call him "Uncle Jeffrey" because he had been friends with my Aunt Gloria since they were kids. Never mind that I had never seen him before in my life. *Okay, Uncle Jeffrey it is!*

Everybody in the yard was doing their respective BBQ things. There was a game of spades at one table. Dominos and smack talk slammed at the other. Horseshoes flew across the way. Soulful R&B moved through the air across clusters of dancing adults. It was 1977, the summer of Stevie Wonder's "Sir Duke" and the kids were putting on a show.

Aunt Gloria and others cheered us on.

"Look at her dance," my Aunt Lindsey said. Aunt Lindsey was my Aunt Gloria's sister-in-law, but just as much my aunt.

The more the grownups watched me the more I turned up the heat. I could feel it all over. I was born with rhythm in my bones and a melody in my muscles.

"She's smart too. She's going to be a doctor," Aunt Gloria bragged. I didn't even know how to spell "doctor." I'm pretty sure I would have spelled it with an "er" back then, but my family was convinced I was genius.

My cousin, Kayla, did not like Aunt Gloria's bragging. As more of the grown ups began to form a circle around to cheer me on, Kayla pushed me. "You ruin every summer."

We were only five so the last four summers must have been doozies for Kayla.

Aunt Lindsey, who was Kayla's grandmother, scolded her. "Apologize to your cousin. We do not treat family like that."

"She's not even in our family. That's not her dad!" Kayla spewed.

I pounced on Kayla like a lion on a dandelion. We rolled on the ground for what was definitely too long for a group of adults to be nearby. I think they let us fight for a minute so I could get my licks in on Kayla. Her ass deserved it. They finally pulled us apart. Angry tears flowed from eyes as I huffed and puffed. I was a kid and the truth hurt.

Aunt Gloria whipped out a red pack of Moore's and lit a cigarette. She took a long drag. Aunt Gloria had an amazing talent to speak full sentences with a cigarette hanging from the corner of her mouth.

"Hell! Half the people out here ain't got the daddy they think." She pointed the cigarette in Kayla's face. "You keep your damn mouth shut. You hear?"

Aunt Gloria cut her eyes at Aunt Lindsey and walked away. I didn't know it at the time, but Aunt Gloria was firing a warning shot at Aunt Lindsey. There were quite a few folks in that backyard that had no idea who their real daddies were. Kayla was one of them. Aunt Lindsey's daughter had a baby by a married man, Kayla's real father…who at the time was over there playing lawn darts and strategically staying far from the commotion.

This was also the first summer I remember meeting Judson Wilson. I was given strict orders not to mention it to Bobby Sparks. Of course! That year my dad picked me up from Nang's house and took me to an amusement park. We laughed and I held his hand as we walked from ride to ride eating cotton candy. He held me tight as we rode through the flashing lights and jumping statues of the haunted house. He didn't seem trifling— whatever that was. We said our goodbyes at the end of the day. I gave him a big hug. It would be twenty years before I got to hug him again.

At this point I've been reconnected to my father for the majority of my adult life. That letter to Bobby Sparks isn't worth the paper it's written on. It would be foolish and quite hypocritical to hold my father accountable for a decision he made when he was twenty-three years old. At that age, we're all still swinging in the dark.

Judson is my dad, the only dad I'll every have. He's the dad God chose for me. He's the Dad I call when I don't feel like working out or when I feel like my work is closing in on me. My favorite thing about Daddy is his laugh. I love to see him laugh until tears fall from his eyes because I do that, too. He tells entertaining stories and has a kind of conventional wisdom that makes the world seem less complicated.

Though he missed my childhood he can certainly boast about the role he's played in the woman I've become. Daddy was the first person to point out how much I liked my husband. He knew before I did. He taught me to be mindful of what I say and write because my words matter. When I look in the mirror, most days I see him and I smile.

Being estranged from your parents isn't the abundant life God wants for you. As much as it depends on you, make peace with them. Make peace with your story. The Bible tells us to honor our parents. There are no caveats and exclusionary clauses that specify our parents need to be award-winning. My story with my parents isn't a fairytale but I've been graced for it. My dad is not exactly Heathcliff Huxtable. Apparently, nobody is, not even Heathcliff Huxtable.

I hope you don't allow your parent's past mistakes to soil your current relationship. I can tell you that you're missing out if you do. You're missing out on love, restoration, and healing. You're missing out on the promise that God made in Exodus 20:12. "Honor your father and mother. Then you will live a long, full life in the land the Lord your God is giving you."

I'm totally going to live to be a hundred years old, maybe a hundred and five.

FIVE

Nothing else provides indisputable evidence that I am a saved, sanctified, Holy Spirit filled Christian like my relationship with my parents. When it comes to Mama and me, it's complicated. My mother is more than a conquerer. She's anointed. That means God has set her apart and chosen her for something special. She is a giant in the pulpit despite her small stature.

We call Mama "NFA"— no fun allowed. She doesn't joke or play around when it comes to God, church, or Christian life. She's not terribly playful when it comes to those things, but she and I manage to laugh hysterically about something every day. Our laughter is a testimony to the goodness of God. It doesn't only testify to the survival of those chaotic years, but it's a testimony of God's love and forgiveness between us.

Our perspectives on the past are very different. She tells stories about how painful it was when I was estranged from her. She talks about how I would come to town and only spend five obligatory minutes with her before going off to do my own thing. She testifies about the times she cried herself to sleep because her children disregarded her. She's not wrong. That's her truth.

My mother has been blessed with dissociative amnesia. She has forgotten many of the details of her life. Some of that is because of the drug use. All of it is due to God's grace, I suppose. While I have certainly been fortunate enough to have mounds of grace in my life, I did not get the grace of erasing my memory. I can recall every ugly detail, most of them vividly. I remember the day she threw her stuff in garbage bags and left. I remember how it felt when she got a one-bedroom apartment with her boyfriend while I slept on Nang's sofa.

I'll never forget the excitement I had on my 21st birthday when I heard her voice on my telephone. It had been a while since we talked.

"Hey Mama." I said with a smile that stretched between my ear lobes.

"Hi love," She quipped in her always upbeat voice. Like most preachers, she's inspiring.

I also recall how it felt the moment I realized that she had not remembered my birthday.

"I was wondering if you can loan me a hundred dollars," she asked.

"I don't have it, Mother."

"Well, that's okay. Alright then."

We said our goodbyes and hung up the phone. I waited two minutes before calling back. She picked up the phone right away, undoubtedly thinking I had changed my mind.

"Mama, it's my birthday."

"It sure is," she quipped.

We sat in silence for a moment to let it sink in. My pain. Her shame.

She said, "Well, alright. I gotta get off here."

I was crushed. I shook it off and lived to love another day. Such is much of my life story.

Shortly after I had Caden, I brought him back to Galia City to meet Nang and the rest of the family. Mama had moved and I didn't know where she lived. My Uncle took me to her new apartment.

When we arrived at Mama's apartment, it took me nearly three minutes to get the baby out of the rear-facing car seat. I was still a rookie. It had already taken two minutes to drape my arms with the diaper bag, my purse, and the "World's Best Grandma" candle I picked up as a gift for my mother. Five minutes later we finally made it to the front door of mama's apartment.

My uncle knocked a few times. There was no answer, but he refused to leave.

"She's not home," I said.

"She's in there. I just talked to her."

He stopped knocking politely and banged on the door with his fist. There was no way my mother was inside, but he refused to leave.

"She's not here," I adjusted the baby and bag collection in my arms to get more comfortable. My biceps started to burn.

My uncle took the diaper bag and the candle. What a relief! He had offered before, but I declined. As usual, I wanted to do it all...the hard way.

"She's here," he said.

He was resolute. There was no doubt in his mind that my mother was home. The baby was getting heavier in my arms with each bang on the door. I became annoyed with my uncle.

"Uncle Mike, Can we—"

The door violently swung open to interrupt me.

"Yes, what?" The disdain on mama's face was undeniable. I stood there with her first-born grandson, whom she had never seen. She gazed at him with a smile, "He's cute as a button," she said.

Mama blocked the doorway with her body. I could see inside the apartment. Her boyfriend— I guess that's who it was— waved a hand to me, "Congratulations."

"Thank you." I swallowed the pain and held back the tears. I turned to my uncle and said, "Let's go."

He barked on my mother. She slammed the door in his face. When we got back to Nang's house, he told her what happened. I cuddled with my baby on the sofa where I used to sleep as a teenager. I held back my tears because I didn't want that sad energy to affect Caden.

You might think it was comforting for people to agree with me. It was just the opposite. It was quite painful to hear Nang and Uncle Mike talk about mama. They agreed that she was a terrible mother and grandmother for rushing us away like that. Misery usually loves company, but that wasn't the case this time. I wanted somebody to tell me I was mistaken. I wanted to be wrong about my mother.

"I don't know what's wrong with your mother, but I know she loves you." Nang said. "She loves you."

There it was again. Just like Grandpa Ted told me about Daddy, Nang was now explaining to me that I was loved despite what it looked like. Do you see how a girl could get a little mixed up about God's love? From my point of view, God's love was no different than the love of my parents. All words. No action. The Bible said God loved me, but I could not see that love in my life.

My journey to discovering God's love was an uphill climb. There was a lot of talk about my parents loving me, but all I received from them was pain. Mama is absolutely right about the way she characterizes our relationship when I was in my late teens and early twenties. She accurately portrays my feelings for her during that time. I saw her as my unruly, undisciplined, prodigal child. While I carried her as my responsibility, I resented being her mother as much as it seemed like she resented being mine.

I can say all of that now without remorse because the end of the story is filled with grace, love, laughter, joy, and yes…still some contentious discussions over our dueling versions of truth. I don't excuse her behavior, but I also don't condemn her.

Regardless of their personal choices, your parents are very important in your development. We chart our life course in agreement with or in opposition to how we were raised. Which one are you? Are your parents the heroes that you emulate, or are they anti-heroes who have taught you a better way to do things?

My mom gives an awesome testimony about the day God told her to love us. On that day the Lord told her, "They can't stop you from loving them." So, she loved us in her own way. From that day she was able to move forward with her life until God reconciled us. She had faith that he would do so.

It's quite amazing when you think about it. She didn't make amends. She didn't apologize. She just waited on God to work it out and He did.

My mom got baptized when she was eleven years old. She tells the story of going in front of the church. They asked her, "Why do you want to follow Jesus?"

"Because I'm tired of being a sinner," she said as the congregation laughed at the cuteness. Even then she saw nothing funny about church, God, or the Christian life. She was annoyed by their lack of reverence for the moment. That's who she is.

People often think I love God because my mom is a preacher. They think I was raised this way. You've read enough thus far to see that's not true. I invited mama to church while she was still in her mess. She came, fell in love with the Lord, and never looked back. She grew and developed spiritually and naturally over time. She eventually became an ordained minister in the AME church and later in the Pentecostal faith. My mother went from being an usher to becoming a powerfully dynamic Apostle. It's an inspiring story of hope and one I'm glad to have witnessed.

You know the way Donald Trump supporters have a dogged allegiance to him and his ability? That's how mama is with me. She thinks I can do anything and tells me so. We laugh until we cry. We love each other fiercely. Our relationship is a three-cord strand with Jesus as the center cord. We have no use for old memories and the devil's dusty resentments. Jesus came into both of our lives and we've been living abundantly ever since.

Can I tell you something? You can't love Jesus and hate your mother. It doesn't work that way. You can't love Jesus and abandon your children. Love doesn't work that way. When you love Jesus, love flows from your heart, your mind, and your life. When you discover the love of Jesus you are drenched in forgiveness and He allows you to see the truth from his perspective— the only one that really matters.

In the Bible, Jesus healed the blind man by putting mud in his eyes. Elisha told Naaman to dip in the dirty Jordan water to cure his leprosy. Let me warn you. It might need to get a little messy before you get healed.

It got a little messy between mama and me. I hosted Thanksgiving at my home. I didn't know it at the time, but this was a ridiculously bad idea. Like I said, I have a habit of doing things the hard way. It's the only way I know. If my endeavors aren't painfully difficult or minimally uncomfortable then I don't know how to move. I suppose it makes me feel strong and courageous. At a minimum, I feel in control.

Mama was upset with me because I wouldn't buy her a four-hundred-dollar Burberry scarf. She called me some names and basically told me I was a terrible daughter. *A terrible daughter?!!*

Mama and I had unfinished business. I welcomed my mom back into my life and pressed any ugly feelings I had beneath the surface. As I said before, she came back into my life with no apologies and no acknowledgment of the pain she had caused my brother and me. I knew what the Bible said. I needed to honor my mother, so I ignored the pain. That wasn't the answer. The love of Jesus heals pain. It doesn't just cover it up. So, on the way to healing, you might get mud in your eyes. That's what happened to mama and me.

Until that Thanksgiving, I thought everything between Mama and myself was cool. I had forgiven her and moved on…or so I thought. She had become a big part of my life again. She decorated my new homes and stayed with us on holidays. We talked on the phone every day. It was all good until she accused me of being a bad daughter.

Shamefully, I called my mother an "ungrateful bitch." I'll never forget the shock on her face. She never dreamed those words would come from me because I had always been the one to coddle and console her. Until that day, I always spoke to her with constrained kindness and obligatory respect.

When I finished telling her about herself, she went to the guest room and cried. My poor husband didn't know what to do so he went up to console her. I was annoyed by his kindness. In my opinion, that was her problem. Everybody coddled her and bailed her out. Everybody rescued her from the consequences of her destructive behavior and habits.

I'll admit that I felt horrible that she was crying. The old habit of coming to her rescue pulled at me. I refused it. While I felt terrible, I also felt a huge burden lift from my heart. My mom had never apologized. She never acknowledged the way she treated me and my brother. She just sashayed back into our lives and took her spot on the maternal throne. I was angry about that, but I let it ride because she's my mother.

Eventually Mama came back downstairs. After throwing more shade as only one's mother can do, she told me stories about her childhood. She apologized that she wasn't a good mother to me. She never realized that I felt responsible for her. She didn't know to nurture me. She never meant to burden me. She didn't know to be protective. In her mind we were a team against Bobby Sparks.

Mama is Nang's youngest child. My mother spent most of her time at my Aunt Elaina's house, her adult big sister. Nang never did for Mama the kinds of things she did for me. They never ate pie on the front porch or watched Imitation of Life together on Saturday afternoons. It was eye opening and hard to believe the stories mama told about my grandmother.

Our grandparents are not the people who raised our parents. By the time they become grandparents, they are wiser, kinder, and have retired from youthful foolishness. Our parents have wounded children on the inside of them, too. So, cut them some slack.

Everybody has a reason for the pain they've felt and an excuse for the pain they've caused. We're flawed, broken human beings whose only hope for a peaceful, functional, abundant life is in Christ Jesus. Let the example of my mother and me be a nudge for you to make peace with the people in your life. Trust God to heal the wounds between you and them. Let his grace flow into every crack in your heart, into every regretful word, and selfish deed. Jesus can fix it. I'm a witness. Mama and I have been besties since that day. Well, about three days after that day.

If the love of God can fix my relationship with my parents, it can fix yours too. If God's unconditional love through me, can swaddle my parents in His grace, unconditional love through you can do it too. Make peace with your parents. Accept who they were. Respect who they are. Believe in who they can be. Whether your parents are still with you or deceased, forgive them. Forgive yourself. Honor your father and mother and watch God pour out blessings on your life. I'm a witness! So is my mama.

SIX

When I married Marcos, Bobby Sparks walked me down the aisle. Honestly, that should have been the first sign of what was to come. When I graduated from college, Bobby Sparks was my only parent who came to town. Granted, he missed the ceremony because he got high and fell asleep in the car. Bobby was a huge part of my early life and he gets a medal for effort, an honorable discharge.

Honoring your parents is the first commandment with a promise. I had clear instruction from the Bible on how to rebuild a relationship with my parents. The path to reconciling my relationship with Bobby Sparks was not quite as obvious. For me, distancing myself from Bobby was necessary for my healing. I needed space from the pain. I needed to live my truth. Having Bobby Sparks in my life meant I'd have to live the narratives of my childhood. That was not an option for me. At least, not a healthy option.

I now conclude that having Bobby Sparks as a dad was better than having no dad at all. I've seen what happens to girls who have daddy issues. He set boundaries and standards for me. He told me that if I got a "C" on my report card I couldn't live at home. Once my art teacher gave me a "C" on a progress report. Bobby Sparks came to school and slapped him. I got a "A" for effort on my report card. I was in the seventh grade before I realized that he couldn't kick me out of the house for getting a "C". By that time, my identity as an honor student was solid and I took a lot of pride in getting straight A's.

Bobby Sparks was around when mama and daddy were not. He certainly added the structure and discipline that shapes my life today. Before you start thinking he deserves a "#1 Dad" coffee mug for raising someone else's child, let me tell you this. He has two other children that he did not acknowledge while he was raising me. In fact, when Bobby married Mama, he had a pregnant girlfriend. If you have children that you don't acknowledge, you are not allowed to participate in the "good dad" contest. You don't qualify. The barrier to entry is claiming and loving all of your children…and that your children know it.

Bobby Sparks always told me that he wasn't going to "sugar coat" life for me and he didn't. That's a large part of how I deal with truth. Give it to me straight in my face with no chaser. That's how I was raised. Both Mama and Bobby Sparks thought thrusting me into adult realities was the right thing to do. It wasn't, but they did what they thought was best.

Despite their chaotic lives, they managed to instill structure and an expectation for excellence into mine. I had curfews that didn't allow me to run the streets. I had chores that had to be done. I can't count the nights Bobby Sparks woke me up to do the dishes long after I had gone to bed. I complained when he made me clean chitterlings or clean up the dog poop. Those are basically the same thing, by the way.

My brother cut the grass, took out the garbage, and had a paper route. By the grace of God, Bobby managed to keep my brother and me out of trouble, off drugs, and focused on achievement. He did all of this despite being out of control, on drugs, and obsessed with my mother.

While my IQ is commendable, I'm sure it would be twenty points higher if I had not suffered a seventeen-year contact high. You know the way people drink bottled water today? That's how Mama and Bobby smoked weed back then. They smoked weed while we watched The Cosby Show and A Different World on family night. While many kids were charged with bringing their father a beer from the kitchen, we were charged with fetching the weed tray or a bag of cocaine from the refrigerator.

Mama and Bobby Sparks got high. They got super-duper, locked in the room, paranoid, peeking out of the blinds high for days at a time. They fought. They watched porn...obviously loud enough for me to know this. Though there were family vacations, great Christmases, and July 4th cookouts to remember, those positive moments are buried under the painful memories that dominate my early life. It's fair to say that it wasn't all bad. It's also important to say that there was too much bad for the good things to matter...at least to me.

I'd go to church on Sundays and cry. One Sunday I decided that I wanted to follow Jesus. I came home excited to tell my parents. Bobby was not having it. No daughter of his would be a part of that mess. He asked me why I wanted to get baptized and I told him that I believed in Jesus. "Don't you?" I asked.

He answered. "I don't believe there has ever been a man to walk this earth any greater than me."

Are you kidding me?!! We didn't have to go all the way back to Jesus to find a man greater than Bobby Sparks. We could simply scan the block for a drug-free man that didn't beat his wife. Bobby may have been greater than the drug addict who let his wife and children go hungry. But Jesus? Nah. John the Baptist said he couldn't carry Jesus' sandals, but Bobby Sparks felt like Jesus was no better than him.

Jesus was way better than Bobby Sparks. I had known this since I was about eight years old and I was confused as to why Bobby didn't know it, too. I sat there, not blinking. I waited for him to say he was just joking. He never did. Bobby believed he was just as great as Jesus.

Bobby Sparks stopped me from getting baptized that year. Pastor Jack, the youth minister, came to the house to change Bobby's mind. *Poor Pastor Jack!* That didn't go well. I looked out the window and watched Pastor Jack get in his car with a red face. I wasn't sure if he was embarrassed, frightened, or if Bobby had slapped him like my art teacher.

About a year or so later, I finally got baptized without telling my parents. Yes, I had to keep it a secret. The church didn't tell them until it was over. Pastor Jack worked with Nang to get it done, of course. Bobby Sparks' opposition to my faith confirmed what I believed about him.

When I was twelve years old, Bobby's face literally transformed in front of my eyes. He turned into a demon with hard-angled features and a mouth full of canine teeth. His eyes turned to fire and the shape of his face morphed. It was so real that I ran out of the house, slamming the door behind me. I ran up the street at full speed as the devil chased me down. I was much older before it occurred to me that I was probably high. I was hallucinating from the contact high. Probably, but not definitively.

Bobby Sparks blasphemed the Lord regularly. If you don't know what that means it means every other sentence had a "GD" in it. The sentences in between those had something like "Jesus [effing] Christ." Bobby Sparks beat my mother more times than she can luckily remember. He spanked my brother out of frustration often. By "spanked" I mean the 1982 beatings y'all used to get that would land parents in jail today. I say "y'all" because he never beat me like that. My mom only gave me two physical spankings in my entire life. I deserved both. But I got emotionally whipped every time my mother or brother was beaten. I'm an empath and it was torture for me to live under such volatility.

When I was in the first grade the teacher called my parents to school because I cried all the time. I was labeled as "sensitive" and later in my life I was deemed, "hypersensitive." I worked very hard in therapy, with personal develop tools, and prayer to manage this trait of my personality. It's the gift of mercy. I feel…a lot. I feel what you feel. So much so, that I have to discern what I actually feel. I have the gift of discernment, too. Now, if you add the powerful gift of mercy and the mysterious "knowing" of discernment, mix it with lies, secrets, abandonment, and abuse… you have yourself one giant ball of chaos ready to explode.

The worst moment between Bobby Sparks and I happened when I was fifteen. I'm not sure about the brand of chaos for the day but Bobby Sparks said to me, "If you don't like it, get out."

I went upstairs and packed a bag. When I trotted my sassy-self back down the stairs, Bobby was waiting for me at the bottom post like a gargoyle. "Where are you going?" he asked.

"You told me to get out." I grinned in a way that only an irreverent teenage girl can do.

He looked at me and saw it. I had lost my fear of him. We locked eyes and mine were like an AR 15 shooting into right into his face.

"You little bitch!" he snarled.

Whop!!! He rang the side of my head and knocked me back up the stairs. That's right, not down the stairs. He hit me so hard he knocked me back up the stairs and I lost hearing in my left ear. This is an important detail because to this day he'll say he hit me with his left hand. He did not. You can't hit me on the left side of my face with your left hand. He hit me. Hard. It was the first time. I wasn't having it, and neither was my mother.

Mama jumped on him like a mad woman. I had never seen her stand up for herself. This was different. She wasn't defending herself; she was defending me. I'm not sure how the next three to five minutes happened. Do you remember that ball of chaos waiting to explode? It exploded.

I turned into a rabid dog. Somehow Mama and I whipped Bobby's ass that day. I know I said I wouldn't cuss but that is the best way for me to describe it. It was a straight up ass whooping. As if he were paralyzed, he wasn't fighting back. He wasn't shouting expletives. He didn't use the Lord's name in vain. Maybe, he was in shock.

Bobby cried as I punched the side of his face in a flurry. Mama and I were like two hyenas eating a lion. The whole time there was a loud thumping in my ears. The side of my face swelled in pain. Needless to say, that was the last time Bobby every laid a hand on me. It was the first and last time.

I inserted myself into my parents' wars and was always able to bring Bobby back from the jungles of Vietnam into the present moment. One of those wars has greatly shaped my faith and how I engage with chaos.

Bobby was beating my mother in the dining room, though I'm sure he thought he was twenty miles north of Saigon. He had her trapped in the corner. He punched, slapped, and kicked her. I grabbed my brother and took him to the entrance of the room. I was nine. He was six. I told him to sing.

"What a mighty God we serve. What a mighty God we serve. Angels bow before Him. Heaven and earth adore Him. What a mighty God we serve." We sang and clapped our hands.

Bobby began to come to himself. "Why are you doing that?"

"Don't stop." I told my little brother. He clapped his little hands and kept singing. I sang louder and clapped harder. Tears streamed from my eyes and I sang through clenched teeth. Bobby Sparks was so perplexed that he stopped beating Mama. He lit a joint and told us to go to our rooms. We gladly obliged.

Our song wasn't necessarily against Bobby. In fact, it helped free him from the grips of evil that had a hold on him that day. That was the day I learned that the devil gets confused when you praise God in chaos and pain. I've been doing it ever since. When a painful memory or terrible mistake from my past pops in my head, I say, "Thank you God. Use it for your glory, my good, and the good of others."

Sometimes I have to say it a few times before the knot in my stomach goes away.

Evil tries to convince you that God doesn't love you. It wants you to believe God doesn't care about you. In those moments, sing a song of praise or just simply say, "Thank you God." It works. I promise.

The whole point of evil is to pull you away from God. If you praise God in chaos, evil gets no satisfaction. The devil will go about his business seeking someone else to devour. I'm not trying to freak you out or get too deep. I just need you to know that Satan is real and he's not a cute little character with a pitchfork. He hates God and anybody who loves God.

Bobby Sparks went to Vietnam at eighteen. He came back and married my mom. He was a coke dealer who smoked marijuana to deal with the anxiety of war. PTSD wasn't a thing back then, but he had it bad. Marijuana led him to cocaine which ultimately led to Bobby and Mama freebasing in their room for days at a time. They were middle-class crackheads who made their kids do chores and get good grades.

He's not a villain in my story. He's a victim. The devil used him. Uncle Sam used him. Even Mama used him for what she needed at the time. The grace of God in my life allowed me to see Bobby for who he really is and it allowed me to appreciate that like all of us, Bobby was created in the image of God.

Everybody has a reason for the pain they've felt and the pain they've caused.

Bobby Sparks was a basehead that went to work every single day. He was a drug dealer that taught us to make an honest living. He worked hard as a chemical operator and retired with full benefits. Functional drug addiction is a real thing. I've seen it close-up and personal.

I'm grateful that God gave me a father in the house. I've seen what happens to fatherless daughters and I'm glad I had some structure in my life. I'm grateful I had a crazy, out of control dad that told me I was smart, beautiful, and capable of anything. I had a dad who loved me the best way he knew how. My brother and I are products of "do as I say not as I do" parenting. By the grace of God, it produced some positive results.

My childhood and adolescence give me a strong connection with Joseph, Jacob's son, in the Bible. A lot of bad things happened to him. He was betrayed by family and friends. He had a lot of people to forgive. His words in Genesis 50:20 summarize my childhood. "You intended to harm me, but God intended it all for good. He brought me to this position so I could save the lives of many people."

This is the life I was given. I was graced for it and I remain in this grace. I had a less than optimal childhood that wasn't "sugar-coated." I suffered much pain and disappointment in the early years of my adult life. Despite the persistent feeling that God didn't love me very much, I made my way to New Jubilee Church. That's when this faith thing got real. But we'll get to that a little later.

SEVEN

Faith and family should be the two most important things in our lives. Family can be complicated. It has been complicated since the beginning of time. I think our family has developed a genuine, deeply abiding love for one another because we are battled-tested... particularly at Thanksgiving.

As it turns out, that fourth Thursday in November holds the most tumultuous— and now hilarious— memories of our family. Let's see, there's the Thanksgiving when my aunt got mad and sat in the car for the entire dinner. The one when Mama and Uncle Mike rebuked each other across the table...

"Get behind me Satan," he said.

"You're the demon," she said.

"No, you're the demon," he said.

"No! You are the demon," she said.

"Nope. You're the demon," he said.

This went on for about ten minutes with various inflections and punctuations of the same sentence. It was wildly entertaining to watch. The argument ended with my mom leaving. On her way out the door she declared, "I'll never step foot in this house again."

The next morning, my uncle made eggs, biscuits, and turkey gravy. As if we don't eat enough on Thanksgiving, my family has breakfast together Friday morning before we hit the streets to shop and catch a movie.

While Uncle Mike was cooking, the doorbell rang. I walked to the door with a sly grin because I already knew who it was. I opened the door and there was mama, ready for our annual outing. We burst into wide mouth laughter.

"That must be your mama," Uncle Mike shouted from the kitchen. He laughed, too.

There was the year my brother and his wife were in passive-aggressive conflict the entire weekend, making everyone uncomfortable. There was the year my middle brother cleared the table with this story about having sex with an Argentinian stripper. One year, mama undercooked the sweet potatoes. One by one, we snuck to the trash and buried them. When she caught us, she threw the rest of the food out in protest. "Y'all don't like my food? Fine!"

We had Chinese food for Thanksgiving that year.

My personal favorite is the year Mama and Aunt Vicky went to war over different church doctrines. I'm pretty sure I'm the only person in the family who thinks this is number one. Everyone else would probably choose the year I went off on Mama. If I weren't the ringmaster of that circus, I'd probably choose that one too. It's the only Thanksgiving that has a name, "Ukulwa," which means "fight" in Xhosa.

Similar to the BC/AD definitions in history, my family discusses timing in context of that dreadful Thanksgiving when I called my mother an ungrateful bitch. "It was the year after Ukulwa" or "Uh-uh, that was before Ukulwa."

This conflict between Mama and Aunt Vicky happened a few years after Ukulwa. My mother was hosting Thanksgiving at her house. Everybody sat around the table in good conversation and laughter. It had been oddly peaceful for a family Thanksgiving so far. There were Baptists and Presbyterians, an Apostolic, a Pentecostal, and my cousin the agnostic.

Honestly, the table was ripe for conflict. Mama, a Pentecostal minister. Aunt Vicky, a staunch African Methodist Episcopalian parishioner. Uncle Mike was an Apostolic deacon. Uncle Mac believed that as long as you were a "good person" you could get to heaven. At the time, I considered myself simply "Christian" and was in vigorous opposition to any denominational label. My brothers and my husband attended Baptist church and were pretty indifferent to the nuances being discussed at the moment. My cousin Leah was exploring Buddhism at the time. She kept her peace. My cousin Chucky had just graduated from seminary. He was now an agnostic, bordering on atheist.

I'm not sure what started it, but it ended with Aunt Vicky telling my mother— the pound for pound holiness heavyweight champion of the world... "You need to read your Bible."

One big, collective gasp from the rest of us sucked the oxygen from the room. Apostolic Uncle Mike looked at me. "Uh-Oh."

I unintentionally held my breath so long that I got dizzy. "It's on now," I exhaled and buried my face in my napkin for a quick prayer.

The three Baptists, my husband and brothers, got up from the table to seek cover in the adjacent room. They made sure to stay close enough to hear and see the action though. My cousin Chucky ate his food in anticipation. He was quite delighted to prove his point about "all this religious mess."

My mother stomped away from the table. She returned with a Bible the size of a pizza oven. I spewed my water across the table in laughter at the very sight of it. That made Mama even more furious. She cut her eyes at me and I zipped my mouth quicker than I zip my purse on the subway.

I already told you that Mama doesn't think God, faith, and church are funny. Apostle don't play that. Mama and Aunt Vicky argued their beliefs until the rest of us were exhausted.

Well actually, Aunt Vicky couldn't insert three words into mama's well-trained, well-studied, ordained opinion. Mama spewed more biblical knowledge than Aunt Vicky could handle. Some of it not applicable to the argument, but it was biblical truth, nonetheless.

Aunt Vicky sounded like the DJ was scratching... "Well, I believe..." she said.

Mama overtalked her.

"I…I…I believe…"

Again, Mama took her down.

"I…I believe…

Mama shut it down. Then…

A melodious voice rang from the adjacent room. "I believe…I…I… I believe that children are the future. Teach them well and let them lead the way."

My brother hopped on the karaoke machine to help Aunt Vicky break through Mama's exegetical power. Everyone burst into laughter, except Mama. Even my agnostic cousin thought that was pretty funny. Mama slammed the Bible shut and stormed out. "Y'all gon' miss it."

The Bible has more family drama than a Tyler Perry movie and it's just as entertaining. Conflict between spouses and sibling rivalries are nothing new. Cain killed Abel in Genesis 4. Family conflict is almost as old as the world itself.

"Even with the woman who lies in your embrace, guard the words of your lips. For a son dishonors his father; a daughter rises up against her mother…a man's enemies are the members of his own household."

Yikes! That's Micah 7:5-6. Poor Micah goes on to say in verse 7, "But as for me I watch in hope for the Lord, I wait for God my savior my God will hear me."

You can't get rid of your family so you might as well lean on the Lord to deal with them.

I love my fragmented, disjointed family. We often joke that we don't have a family tree. We have family hedges. We don't just span upward, but my family is wide and extended. It's the family the Lord gave me. Your definition of family may be limited to blood relatives. Maybe you see family as the people with whom you choose to build a life, regardless of bloodline. Most of us have friends that have become family, as well. That's Framily.

Jesus had parents and siblings, but he said that his family was all those who obey the Lord. When his mother and brothers wanted to talk to him while he was teaching, he replied, "Who is my mother? Who are my brothers?" Then he pointed to his disciples and said, "Look, these are my mother and brothers. Anyone who does the will of my Father in heaven is my brother and sister and mother!" That's Matthew 12:48-50.

You are not alone in wishing you could trade in your drunk uncle for Uncle Phil from *The Fresh Prince*. Who wouldn't love to have the super cool Zoey Johnson from *Blackish* as their big sister? I'm telling you right now. I'd take any of those sad little Pearsons from *This is Us* as my cousins. They need a hug…and so do the people in our families.

Obviously, there are family members who simply cannot have a lot of space in our lives. It is important to define (and redefine) our relationships with family members. The Bible is clear that we must honor our parents. It gives us clear instruction to love and honor our spouses and train our children up in the ways of the Lord. Everybody else in our family falls into two categories: people we love and people we love because Jesus said so.

If you want to be a good Christian, you can't hate anybody. You can't even hate the person who caused you the most harm. Hate has no place in the Christian heart. It's a foreign virus that infects our hearts and then our lives. Notice that I said a "good" Christian. You can be a bad Christian. It's a thing. It has nothing to do with drinking, cussing, or the amount of cleavage that flows from your push-up bra. The difference between a good Christian and a bad one is love.

You've got to love everyone, especially your family. It's not always easy, but… I guess there are no "buts." It's not always easy. I'll leave it there.

Top five Emcees of all time? Kobe or Lebron? Prince or Michael Jackson? Franks or Louisiana hot sauce? Something starts the debate and before you know it somebody's sitting in the car. When this happens in my family, or yours, we aren't really arguing about hot sauce. Mama is the youngest of her siblings. As much as she was fighting for her doctrinal beliefs that day, she was also fighting to be heard among her older siblings who often diminish her. The Gospel is the one place where she could assert some authority in our family.

Unresolved issues will make their way from your heart to your lips. "What you say flows from what is in your heart." That's Luke 6:45. We never say things we don't mean. We say things we don't mean to say. I've said terrible things I meant in the moment. I just never intended to say them out loud for anyone else to hear.

We let our emotions carry us away. It happens. Thank God for the courage to apologize when we are wrong. Thank God for the grace to forgive others when they have wronged us. None of our families are perfect but let me tell you something about family. Families are like Noah's Ark. We all know the story. Noah brought all of the animals onto the ark in pairs, one male and one female. He was on the boat with his wife, his sons, and their wives. It rained for forty days and forty nights, but Noah was trapped on that boat with his family for twelve and a half months.

On the first day of the new year, ten and a half months after the flood began, the floodwaters had almost dried up from the earth. Noah lifted back the covering of the boat and saw that the surface of the ground was drying. Two more months went by, and at last the earth was dry! Then God said to Noah, "Leave the boat, all of you—you and your wife, and your sons and their wives. - Genesis 8:13-15

I'm pretty sure it was stinky on that ark because the zoo stinks and the animals are outside. Can you imagine the amount of poop that built up over those months? I'm sure it was nothing compared to the frustration and conflict that a year of being sheltered in place produced.

The ark was not a luxury stay at the Fontainebleau. I bet Noah and his family had plenty of issues. I'm absolutely sure it was stinky. However, the ark was the vessel God used to keep Noah and his family safe. It wasn't perfect but it was exactly where God wanted them to be in order to survive.

Sit with that for a moment. Read it again if you must. The ark is where you survive.

My family is my ark. My family has gentle doves and stubborn asses. Poop piles up. I clean it and more poop is yet to come. My family isn't perfect. Neither is yours. God gave us the family we have so we can be who he created us to be. Your family is a part of your purpose. If you want to live abundantly, you'll have to make peace with the family God gave you.

I'm the only child of my mother and father together. I share a mother with one brother. I share a father with my other three siblings. There are two fathers and three mothers among us. Two of my brothers have siblings that are not my siblings. It's delightfully messy. Miraculously and perfectly purposed, my husband has a similar sibling situation. All of our siblings are a family. Our children are cousins. We did not let the mishaps and hangups of our parents soil our lives.

I live the truth of my family proudly and boldly for my children to see. I have accepted the family God has given us and it is my ark. It can get a little messy if we let the "stuff" from our parents spill over into our lives. My father doesn't acknowledge my brother. My brother doesn't deal with his mother. My sisters-in-law are disconnected from each other but connected to my husband. While my sons have a relationship with their Grandaddy, my nieces have never met him. It's messy, but I'm graced for it. I pray to be better than the last generation. I pray to be honest with myself and my children. I vow to stay connected and united with the family God has given me, as stressful as it may be.

Here's my advice to you… God has given you grace to be in your family. Remain in His grace. Fix the broken pieces and mend the cracks as it pertains to you. Call your sister. Make peace with your brother. Forgive your cousin. Climb back into your ark so the storm doesn't take you out. Do it now. Do it today. Don't let another broken branch root division and dysfunction into your family. Generational curses are real. You can break them or perpetuate them.

EIGHT

They say that people come into your life for a reason, a season, or a lifetime. "They" are wrong. You don't spend your lifetime with anyone but yourself. You might as well get cool with you because you're stuck with you. A reason? Certainly! Even if only for a season, people have a reason for being in your life. "Reason" and "season" are not mutually exclusive. If you're blessed, you'll find some friends to journey with you for a significant portion of your life. I am blessed in that regard.

Nang and I often talked about friends and friendship. She'd ask me about my friends. This one is mad at me. We're not talking to that one. That's how it goes with adolescent girls. Drama. Always. Whenever I'd get hurt by someone who I thought to be my friend, Nang told me, "You're blessed if you find one friend in life."

Nang's definition of "friend" was distinct. She believed that a friend is someone you can trust without question. A friend is someone who loves you unconditionally. A friend is someone who would never hurt you and always wishes you well. Nang had one friend, Miss Nadine.

One day I walked into the kitchen and saw a sour expression on Nang's face. "Let me ask you something," she said.

For seventeen years I was told to stay out of grown folks' business. My moment had arrived. I quickly sat down at the table next to Nang. "What's up?" I asked.

Nang pointed to a Tanqueray box on the floor. The night before, Grandpa Sam had bought pizza and pop for my cousins and me. If you don't know what "pop" is, it's soda…Coke, Sprite, 7-up, etc. The pizza shop loaded all of the goodies into that box. Apparently, Miss Nadine saw the empty box on the floor and said two words that very much offended Nang.

Miss Nadine said, "Oh spirits?"

That's it. That's all she said.

Nang was wounded by the two potential realities of her friendship with Miss Nadine. The first reality was that after so many years of friendship Miss Nadine didn't know Nang very well. The second possible reality was even more hurtful to my grandmother. Miss Nadine thought she had busted Nang drinking liquor. Apparently, she showed some delight in doing so. This was the worst of the two realities.

As Nang talked at me about the situation, I realized that she was not interested in my opinion at all.

I offered my perspective anyway. "Maybe she was just asking." I said innocently.

"Don't be naive. I know Nadine and I know what she meant. We've been friends for forty years."

"Okay," I said and got up from the table because it was obvious that I was no longer needed. Nang's eyes illuminated her pain. I wanted to cheer her up.

"Miss Nadine is your one true friend so I'm sure she didn't mean it that way."

I gave Nang a kiss on the cheek.

Nang twisted her face at me. She didn't roll her eyes, but it felt like she did. "Jesus is my one true friend. Nadine was my one friend in life."

The "true" and the "was" were punctuated with clarity and deep meaning. Nang and Miss Nadine stayed cool, but she was no longer considered a friend. She was merely an acquaintance, someone who stopped by for sweet tea and pie on Saturdays.

John 15:13 says, "There is no greater love than to lay down one's life for one's friends." We may have people who say that they would die for us, but Jesus actually did. This doesn't make Jesus our only friend. It does mean that he is our very best friend. To Nang's point, Jesus is our one true friend.

I have an amazing sister circle of friends. We share everything. We delight in the joys of motherhood. We mourn together in the tragedy of loss. We celebrate new homes and new jobs. We pray with each other and for each other. My crew is dope. It is full of amazing, brilliant, beautiful, women of God. Some of them are jumping for Jesus like me while others are coming along in their faith. We're doing life together. I consider them "friends".

I don't think Nang expected perfection from Miss Nadine because they had disagreements over the years. I think she expected reciprocity. It's natural for us to desire to reap the love we sow. If you are a good friend, you will absolutely reap the rewards of friendship. However, you may not reap that friendship from where you sow it.

All of your friendships will not be fruitful and lasting. Some are for a reason. Others, for just a season. While I don't think Nang was right about having only one friend in your life, I don't believe she was wrong about the need to redefine friendship when necessary. I have learned to limit my interaction with those who produce negative thoughts, feelings, emotions, or behavior in my life. I reposition them.

Let me be clear. You are solely responsible for the way you think, behave, and feel. However, the people in your life can have a powerful influence in how you live. Negative stimuli from outside can affect who you are on the inside. If you want to be a positive, uplifting, loving person then you'll have to limit your exposure to negative, angry, mean people…even if you love them…especially if you love them.

If you're trying to stop drinking, your drunk friends need to fall back. If you want to hold your marriage together, you might need to silence the single friends who encourage you to divorce. If you want to live on purpose, you must be intentional about who you let into your life and the roles they play.

Jesus had followers, disciples, a squad, and a crew. Each group served a specific purpose and had a different kind of relationship with him. I've built my social life like Jesus— except it would be way better if I could turn water into wine. Because we always run out of wine. Some of my friendships, I've painfully redefined. I've been forced to turn away from others and accept that our season is over. I'm blessed to have good friends who have consistently remained with me for over thirty years. I also have new friends from the last decade who feel like they've been with me forever. In my opinion, friends are a gift from God.

In the wisdom of my adulthood, I've moved beyond Nang's definition of friendship. Nang believed a friend was someone you can trust without question. The Bible instructs us to only put our trust in God. So, I trust God to be involved in my friendships. I trust him to protect me and to create the reasons and seasons for the people in my life. Nang's definition of friend was someone who loves you unconditionally. Human beings are flawed and our capacity to love is directly related to our relationship with God, who is love. Our friends may profess love for us when things are going well. When things get sticky, you may find that their love is conditional, or worse, not genuine.

Some people enjoy being your friend when life is hard. They are unable to remain your friend when your life gets better. You may find it easier to be friends with people when you are happy with your own life. When things aren't going well in your life, you may find it challenging to be a good friend to others. Your friends aren't perfect. Neither are you. Friendship requires grace, mercy, and prayer.

We know that natural seasons change. Winter, summer, spring, and fall each return in God's marvelous cycle. Sometimes, our friendships do the same. That's the story of Jen and me. We've had seasons of high praise in the fullness of the Holy Spirit. We've also had times that were not so much in Christ Jesus. We've prayed for others and fought together. We've fought each other and needed much prayer. I led Jen to Christ when we were undergraduates. Years later, Jen was the angel who came to me during my divorce with a word of encouragement from the Lord. Talk about reaping what you sow. Thanks God!

In all fairness, Jen should have been the one to console me during my divorce. It was kind of her fault I married

Marcos in the first place. One night, Marcos walked me back to my car after studying together. As I stuck my keys into the door, a hand grabbed my ankles from beneath the car. Scalding fear filled my body in a flame. It was Bonita, Marcos' ex-girlfriend. She had been stalking me for weeks. She showed up outside my classrooms and at the restaurants where we ate. She once hid in the bushes outside the library and jumped out to simply scare me. I hit her in the face with a book before I even knew it was her. I apologized and explained that I was abused as a child, so my "fight" was much more instinctive than my "flight".

That night, I left Bonita and Marcos to work out their issues in the parking lot. The farther I drove, the hotter the flame burned inside me. I went straight to Jen's dorm for backup. "If I don't fight her, she's going to keep coming for me." Nang taught me that.

I slid off my designer sweater and cute little mini skirt. Jen gave me sweatpants and a pink t-shirt with "Cutie Pie" written across on the chest. We got in my car and drove back to find Marcos and Bonita still beefing in the parking lot. As it turns out, Marcos had just had sex with Bonita the night before. I didn't much care about that. He and I weren't having sex yet so "do you."

Jen stepped in and got in Marcos' face. "You better make a decision." I think she called him the N-word, too. I know she did.

I stood there glaring at Marcos, disgusted. I looked back and forth between him and Bonita. She was low-class and not attractive at all. It was an indicator of how low his self-esteem was at the time. In fact, I once explained to someone that Bonita hated me because I was married to her ex. I'll never forget the look on the guy's face. "You date someone who was with her?" He couldn't believe it.

Up to that point, all of my fights had been explosions of emotion in a single moment. I didn't know how to do this. We all just stood there in a circle, looking silly. I wasn't going to fight over Marcos. I wasn't that into him at the time. I would fight to defend myself, though. That's exactly what happened.

Jen forced Marcos' hand. "Who do you want to be with?"

Marcos is no dummy. He's also articulate so he began his monologue. "Well, I was with one of you. Then I met the other one. But I fell in love with one of you."

I stood there with my lips twisted. *What a load of crap!*

"Who Marcos? Who do you love?" Jen demanded an answer. I knew the answer.

Bonita pressed the issue. "Yeah, say who. Tell her who you love?"

I cut my eyes at Bonita. She was crazier than I knew she was. Marcos stood in silence.

I shook my head, "Never mind. Let's go." I took a step to walk away. Marcos pulled me back into an embrace.

"You're choosing her?" Bonita shrieked.

She took a swipe at me and a bell rang in my head. Bonita fought for Marcos. I defended myself. She lost the fight and the man. Ironically, it made her the winner in the long game.

Jen and I laugh about it now. If she had not given me those sweatpants, I may have never married Marcos. It's all Jen's fault. At least that's my story and I'm sticking to it…in uproarious laughter.

At this point Jen and I share thirty years of friendship with Christ at the center of our lives and of our sisterhood. Jen and I have redefined and repositioned over the years. We've been friends and frenemies. Through Christ, we always find our way back to being sisters.

The Bible says we are one body with many parts. The ankles and the ear lobes don't hang out together. You can distance yourself from Christian friends for a season. You cannot abandon them. I have developed purposeful friendships with women from various aspects of my life. My sorority sisters are delightful. My "Bridge Crew" and I have been friends since the summer after high school. We still take annual trips together. I have been blessed to make lasting friendships with coworkers beyond our time working together. One of my very special friends is a woman who worked for my husband when we were dating. Once we married, she and I became friends. We have our own thing now. He's not even in it.

My Beantown friends are ride or die. I still laugh aloud when I think of the shenanigans with my Detroit friends. My hometown squad is forever. Connecticut comes through for me on a moment's notice. New York and Jersey hold it down.

Counter to Nang's warning, I consider myself to have lots of friends. My days have been filled with love from friends that have sustained me through the toughest times of my life.

Nang wasn't wrong about many things, but I think she was wrong about isolating herself to just one friend. I think she asked too much of Miss Nadine and I think her definition of "friend" was unrealistic. Relationships grow and get stronger through managing conflict and enduring hardship. I don't always agree with my friends and I know I get on their nerves with all of my stuff, too. The definition of friendship is not a pain-free relationship where there is unconditional love. Friendship is the journey to unconditional love. It's the laughter and the tears.

You may think that keeping a small circle is the way to protect yourself from getting your feelings hurt. Nang only had one friend and still got her feelings hurt. It's hard to let go of our fear and ignore our insecurity, but that's what it takes to be a good friend. Trust the good people in your life and lean into them. Accept the love and care that God is sending you through friendships.

My friends and friendships have been an integral part of developing my faith. My faith has been an integral part of understanding my friendships. If you aren't as spiritually healthy as you'd like to be, take a look at your social circle. Are those people stakeholders helping you become your best self or stake drivers, impeding your progress? You may need to reposition yourself.

NINE

I have a father, a husband, two sons, three brothers, five uncles, seven nephews, and a bunch of male cousins. Friendships with men come natural to me. However, having guy friends can be tricky. Be careful. While I have been a persistent "gal pal" and maintained healthy friendships with male friends, I also married one of them. Like I said, male-female relationships are tricky. I can tell you that they work, but only when neither of you has an ulterior motive.

Gentleman, not every woman who smiles at you wants to sleep with you. Some women are happy, pleasant, joyful beings who have a love for humanity. Otherwise, she might just be having a good day. In the case that she's having a bad day, don't try to use it to your advantage. By the time we're thirty, women have heard most of what you have to say. So, say less.

A guy once told me that I was an angel who fell from heaven.

"That's offensive," I said and left him puzzled in the potato chip aisle. For the record, Satan is the angel that fell from heaven so stop saying that to women. It's not a compliment.

One afternoon, I returned to the office frustrated. A coworker noticed my disposition and asked me about the weather. "It's hot!" I quipped.

He said, "I asked about the weather, not you."

While it was clever, I had heard it before…multiple times. I rolled my eyes and kept stepping. About twenty minutes later he came to my office and apologized. Apology accepted! We became friends.

Ladies, sometimes men genuinely befriend you because you're cool, but not their type. Most of my guy friends fall into this category. While I may be physically appealing to them, their brittle egos require something different. Not better. Not worse. Just something different.

Take my friend Lenox for instance. He was extremely picky. He knew what he wanted in a woman. He didn't care who judged him for it or how long it took to find her. He invited me to dinner to discuss the amazing woman he had been dating for the past four months. More specifically, he wanted to know how to break up with her without looking like a jerk. When I asked why he wanted to break it off, he told me that he thought a wife should be "financially and intellectually inferior" to her husband.

"So... broke and silly?" I asked.

"No, just not self-sufficient."

"Geez! I'll never marry again."

Lenox offered up names from my casual dating roster. "You've got Max."

I quickly shook my head. "He thinks reading is lame."

"How about Eric? He's double Ivy."

"And just borrowed a hundred dollars."

I dipped a french fry into Lenox's ketchup with a sigh. His eyes widened. He gently grabbed both of my wrists. Lenox had a germ phobia and refused to hold anyone's hand. He offered the name of one of his good friends, a brilliant physicist... "Richie!"

Richie was intellectually stimulating and financially astute. Lenox thought Richie was perfect for me.

I disagreed. "Literally, the most frustrating first date of my life."

"He's a good dude, though." Lenox pleaded. "Give him another shot."

"He thinks Jesus was... and I quote... an awesome magician."

My face contorted. We sat in silence.

"What about—"

"Nope," I said.

"Ohhh, how about —"

"Absolutely not."

A sense of despair settled in my tummy. If Lenox felt this way, how many other men secretly felt like I would be too much for them? Or worse, how many men needed an inferior wife and didn't know it? I was doomed. I pondered my dilemma.

"You're smarter than me," I winked with a wry grin.

"We both know that's not true..." Lenox chuckled.

I looked across the table with doe eyes and a contrived naivety.

"See. That right there." Lenox shook his head. "You'll have me robbing banks for you."

We laughed and finished our dinner. Lenox broke up with his girlfriend. He probably dated a hundred women after that. Lenox broke up with a woman because she snacked too much, and he was afraid she'd get fat. He broke up with another because she laughed loudly with an open mouth...as if you can laugh with your mouth closed.

I hooked Lenox up with one of my closest girlfriends, but she wasn't up for the challenge. He was too difficult. I hooked him up with my sorority sister. He said that she didn't excite him. Whatever that means. Lenox wanted a woman who liked what he liked. Additionally, she could not be passionate about anything he disliked. Oh, and Lenox hates fake nails, lashes, wigs, and weaves.

"So let me get this straight. You want your wife to be a natural beauty who will never get fat. She has to earn six figures but still need you. You want her to be smart enough that you don't have to worry about her but not so smart that she doesn't need your guidance."

I thought saying it out loud would jolt Lenox into reality.

"Yes," Lenox said proudly. "That's it."

I gave it another try. "She has to like your music, your food, and your movies. And you have to do…what exactly?"

"No, she can like different things, but just not the things I hate." He explained.

I folded my arms. "I'm listening."

"Her favorite music can't be country music. She doesn't have to watch football all day, but she can't complain when I do. I need a Betty or Coretta."

"You're ridiculous!" I flicked a splash of water across the table at him

Lenox stuck to his guns and eventually found his wife. To both of our surprise, it was me. Single women ripped their clothes in the streets and tears dripped into appletinis around the nation. Unyielding, uncompromising, and refusing to lower his standards, Lenox married his friend, and I married mine.

The most refreshing thing I find about having male friends is the lack of pretense. Men and women can develop strong, honest friendships without fear of judgement. I think that's what happened with Lenox and me. There was nothing to hide. He already knew my stuff. I was well acquainted with all of his. There were no lies and no misrepresentations. I couldn't play the damsel. He knew better. He couldn't act like he wasn't gawking at asses in the mall. I knew better. When I start concocting an outrageous plan he simply says, "Toyi Elizabeth." It's a whole conversation in two words.

My guy friends, including Lenox, help me understand the way a man thinks…or doesn't think, usually. Men and women are quite different. It is only by the grace of God that we can build lives together. It's why I find real friendship to be the foundation of marriage. In those moments when I thought I could do without Lenox as a husband, I was grieved by the notion of living life without my friend. Lenox is my person. First, he was my friend.

While men and women have many differences, there is a common ground on which friendship can be built. My friend Cary taught me about a man's shame. My friend Tyler taught me about the burden of responsibility a godly man feels to provide. Lee helped me realize that men have deep insecurities despite having broad shoulders. I've learned a lot from my male friendships.

While Lenox and I started as friends and ended up in romance, most times this happens in reverse. There's an immediate attraction between two people but something happens, and the relationship moves into the friend zone. This is the story of Kendall and me.

Kendall and I met at Essence festival in his hometown of New Orleans. When I saw first him approach, he took my breath way. Six-ten, with kind eyes and a head full of silky waves, he was totally my type. He was assertive but not overbearing. He was funny. He was an original.

"First, I want your number," he said. "Then I want to dance with you. Just in case you don't like the way I dance."

That's how he opened. I appreciated the candor and the humor. I had never seen anyone who could bang in the paint and dance beyond a two-step, but Kendall had moves. While we were dancing, he asked how old I was.

I told him. "Twenty-Six."

His face turned ashy. It concerned me.

"How old are you?" I asked in a tone that signaled I was the mother of a five-year-old at the time.

"What difference does it make, yeah?" His accent made my ears smile.

I stopped dancing and folded my arms. It's what I do when I mean business. I stared him down like he had not done his homework and arrived late to class.

"Eighteen," he said.

I nearly fainted.

Kendall had just graduated from high school and strolled into an NBA party like a baller. I had to give it to him. It was brazened. It's something I would have done at his age if I were built like Dwight Howard. Kendall became like a brother to me. I can say this because I have three brothers and know what the relationship entails. It cracks me up when people compare their experiences to something they've never experienced. They say, "She's like sister to me" but have no sisters to even understand what that means. Anyway, I digress.

I talked him through college girlfriends and stayed up with him as he studied for final exams. I made him shoot free throws until he whined, and I chastised him if he didn't have at least four fouls in every game. Kendall graduated on time with a finance degree from the University of Louisiana. He went to work at a top brokerage firm in glasses and a pocket protector. At darn near seven-feet, Kendall was offended when clients and coworkers asked him "Did you play ball?"

A year into the job, Kendall got an offer to play overseas for a few months in the summer. It was an opportunity to make a lot of money in a short time. He was financially astute, more than me. He took a leave from work and headed to New Zealand. We emailed daily and only talked on Saturdays.

One Tuesday, I sent a message that I had booked a trip to the islands for ten days. He called immediately. "No!"

Kendall was younger but he called himself my big brother for obvious reasons. He was fiercely protective of me. He did not want me to go out of the country while he was away. "I'm not comfortable with this, Tee Tee."

"I'll email you every day."

He was irrationally mad at me for going. I emailed him daily for the first six days and he never responded. The last email I sent was "You're being such a baby about this. But that's why I love you."

I called him as soon as I got back. He didn't answer. Three days later I received a call from his mother. Kendall died of a heart attack at twenty-two years old. He died the first day of my trip. I missed his death and burial. His family tried to find me. They waited for as long as they could. I was devastated.

This was the second time God took someone important from me. It was the second time I was not allowed to say goodbye. Like Nang, Kendall died while we were in conflict. This time, my faith was stronger, but not perfect. I was sad and broken, but I wasn't angry. The pain of losing Kendall resurfaced feelings of abandonment. It made me wonder once again if I was destined to lose anything and everyone I loved.

Kendall's death was an important moment in my relationship with Lenox. After Kendall died, I pulled back from Lenox. In hindsight, it likely delayed our marriage by two years. I began to separate myself from people I loved. It was irrational, yet very real to me at the time. It is also the reason that I hashtag "read your bible" weekly on social media. If I had been reading my Bible, praying, and spending time with God daily, I would have had a better understanding of death.

Coming to terms with untimely death is an arduous and most difficult process. With the global COVID 19 pandemic we've experienced more loss than any of us could have ever imagined. Even when the loss is not personal, it touches our humanity and resurfaces the pain of our own losses. Hold on to God in these times.

1 Corinthians 15:55 reminds us that the grave has no victory and death has no sting...for the dead. For us, it hurts. While my heart certainly grieves the loss of friends, family, and strangers, I find comfort in knowing that the dead in Christ are actually much better off than we are. We are left here with pain, sadness, and grief. We are left here to wonder who God is and what on earth He is doing. Meanwhile, our loved ones are kicking it in peace, joy, and everlasting life. They are winning.

I pray that God heal your grieving heart. I've been there. I know the pain of repeated loss. I know the struggle to reconcile the sudden death of a loved one. My attitude about death and my faith in everlasting life has developed from loss. Learn from your losses. Hold on to your faith.

TEN

When I was dating, I had a list of things I required in a man, but the list was stupid. It had characteristics on it like "kind" and "smart." Can I tell you something? Nobody has "mean" and "dumb" on their list. Some traits should just be a barrier to entry.

Before I show you my list, let me tell you how this list came to be. My mother called me after watching an episode of Oprah. "Girl, Oprah was too good today," she said before I could even greet her.

"Hey Mama."

"Ayana said you need a list." And by Ayana she meant Iyanla Vanzant.

"Mmm hmm," I said.

"Let me tell you what's on your list…" Mama proceeded to run down a list of traits she created for my future husband.

Don't giggle. It might be funny now. At the time I was quite annoyed. "Mama, you cannot make a list for me."

"Yes, I can. I know you better than you know yourself."

I didn't get much parental guidance as a teenager, but my adulthood has been filled with enough motherly advice to backpay those years in full. Mama has an opinion on everything in my life from how I organize my kitchen cabinets to which dresses are "too soft" for my personality. So, that's how the list came to be. It was Mama's idea through Iyanla Vanzant by way of Oprah.

I didn't use my mother's list which included "preacher" and "exceedingly wealthy"— two things that are often, and usually should be, at odds with one another. Ignoring my mother's criteria, I sat down with my journal and created a list of my own:

1. Know God
2. Love Children
3. Financially secure
4. Never married and no kids
5. Can't mistake my kindness for weakness
6. Have a purpose
7. Cry about something other than me

Turn to your neighbor and say, "This is the stupidest list ever."

It only has seven traits because seven is the number of completion. How ridiculous! A list this shallow and ambiguous leaves room for eight out of ten clowns to make it into your life. This list is easily manipulated to fit your own rationalizations. It does not offer strong accountability for your choice. I made this list based on my experience at the time. I created the criteria to eliminate things I knew I didn't want, but it wasn't terribly specific in the affirmative.

Know God? Everybody knows God. He's famous! James 2:19 says, "You say you have faith. You believe that there is one God. Good for you! Even the demons believe this and they tremble in terror." I dated a number of church boys in my twenties. Marcos was a church boy. I dated a deacon and a pastor...which is why I knew my mother's list was dead wrong.

Love children? That's silly. Nobody hates children but the devil. What I really wanted was someone who aligned with me on how to raise children. Because I had a "not sugar coated" childhood, I believe kids get to be kids for as long as they can. I think a child's life needs to be Candyland with sprinkles. I let children make snow angels by throwing popcorn all over my living room floor. I let kids drink soda on Christmas Eve and eat junk food on Saturdays. I watch kid TV shows and learn kid dances so my quality time with them is actually valuable.

I intentionally butcher the words to their songs so they can laugh at me. I wanted my children to laugh often and laugh loudly. In my view, children are to be seen and heard. I wanted my children to have something I didn't have…a childhood. "Love Children" was too vague.

Number three is ridiculous because nobody has "broke" on their list. What I required was a man who aligned with my philosophy on money and agreed with the Bible. Don't rack up debt. Save something. Give something. Don't chase money to make you happy. I had already dated someone whom my grandmother would describe as having "too many dollars and not enough sense." So, the amount of money a man earned wasn't the issue. I was more concerned about his relationship with money.

Number four was a keeper. When I was dating, I didn't want to be "a wife." I was determined to be "the wife." I refused to date anyone who had been married or had children. Yes, I was divorced with a young son. My rationale was plain and simple. I had my own drama, and I wasn't signing up for anybody else's.

Hypocrisy? Most definitely.

Wisdom? You darn right! I knew exactly what I was doing. "Never married and no kids" was the best thing on my list.

In retrospect, my dating life was really funny. Let's see…I dated that dude. One night, at dinner with friends, he announced with a toast, "I can't believe I've fallen in love with a Black woman."

He was Black.

I dated a highly regarded chef who wanted to be a deejay.

I dated a deejay who wanted to be an actor.

I also dated an actor who wanted to be a chef.

I dated models, an olympian, and the guy who invented ghosting. I dated a literal brain surgeon and a real-life astronaut. There was the preacher who whipped out a ring and proposed to me after one date at the movies… "I asked God if I could have you and He said yes."

My dating history and "the list" provides plenty of dinner party entertainment. I can laugh at the mistakes of my youth. This list was a big mistake. Let me tell you about the dude that met all of the criteria on the list…and why I ditched the list after him.

Telis was a handsome politician with thirty-two blinding white teeth. We went to the same church. Our pastor introduced us. At the time, he was well into a successful run for mayor. He was the city's golden boy and the youngest to ever get close to the seat. I liked that he had the presence of mind to extend his hand and introduce himself even though his face was plastered all over the city.

About five months into the relationship Telis told our pastor that he wanted to marry me. The pastor's wife overheard his conversation and told me so. I panicked. There was something sneaky about Telis that I couldn't put my finger on. I know what you're thinking. Why did I expect to date an honest, loyal, and trustworthy politician? I'm going to blame it on the unsophisticated innocence of youth.

Telis had given me no reason to distrust him. There were no signs or signals. He picked up the phone whenever I called. He had given me full access to everything in his life. I even had a key to his home to come and go as I pleased. I made a few pop ups, too. I wasn't that naive.

His mother smothered me from day one. His sisters told me things he said when I wasn't around. His biological family and our church family bombarded me with assurance that this relationship was the best thing to ever happen to Telis. To this day, I don't disagree.

One night, Telis took me to dinner at a Michelin restaurant. My heart thumped when the valet opened my door. I knew this was it, and I wasn't ready. My vision blurred. I took a deep breath to avoid thrusting myself into a full-blown anxiety attack. Telis was going to propose, and I needed an out.

At one point in the meal, Telis excused himself from the table. I saw him speak to the maitre d' on the way to the restroom. When Telis came back to the table, I faked a headache so we could leave before dessert. He tried to get me to stay but I really put on a show. Telis asked the waiter to cancel the "surprise dessert" he had ordered, and we left.

We pulled up to my house and sat in the driveway. I decided it was time to tell Telis the whole truth. "I have a confession. Sister told me about your conversation with Pastor."

Telis laughed. "I thought you were going to confess that you faked a headache to keep me from proposing."

I leaned my head on his shoulder. I told him that I could not shake this pit in my stomach. I felt like there was something I didn't know— something big. He assured me that I was wrong.

"You just need time." He understood that I had been wounded. Welled with tears, Telis pulled the ring box from his pocket. "God said you are my wife. I'll wait as long as it takes for you to get comfortable."

This was not the first time I had seen Telis cry. I had seen him cry, overwhelmed with purpose. His passion for politics and improving his city often brought tears to his eyes. So did a really good drama. Telis was amazing with his nieces and nephews. He let the girls paint his nails and he wrestled with the boys, ripping a custom suit. Telis had seven out of seven criteria on the list. A homerun! A slam dunk! A touchdown!

However, something was wrong. I couldn't quite articulate what it was, but I knew it. I simply couldn't get settled in this relationship. I was always uneasy. While he had decided to marry me, I developed a pit in my stomach every time he called.

A stream of tears flowed from his eyes. "It hurts that you don't trust me, but I understand. I will do whatever it takes to earn your trust."

"Can we pray?" I asked.

"Of course," he said. We bowed our heads and clasped hands. Telis led us in prayer as he had done many times. "Heavenly Father, give your daughter the comfort and answers she needs."

Then...

SLAM!!! A loud crash startled us, and glass fell into my lap. Right in the middle of prayer, a bat smashed the front windshield. There was my answer. She was a woman not quite press-worthy, a woman not befitting of an outspoken, Christian politician. She was a broken woman who was tired of being left in the sheets. He told her that he had to remain focused on his goals. He told her that after the election he could take her out in public. He obviously thought very little of this woman and assumed she didn't read the newspapers. I remember the look on Telis' face when the woman slammed the article up against the driver's side window.

She had underlined the quote from Telis in red ink. "The only thing I love more than this city is this woman right here." The quote captioned a photo of Telis and me in matching baseball jerseys. It was a picture of him kissing me on the cheek and me smiling like I had been kissed by the summer moonlight.

She looked at me, "Are you the one from some podunk town?"

This got my attention.

She slammed the bat against the driver's side door. "I thought you said she cusses like a sailor, Telis?" She hit the car again with the bat.

Tells turned greenish gray. Crocodile tears drenched his face. He looked over at me. "Baby," he pleaded.

"You know you said that shit." I jumped out of the car.

Telis wasn't lying. I cussed too much, but that's not the point of this story. Just like Marcos and Bonita, I left the two of them in my driveway to work out their differences. Unlike with Marcos and Bonita, I did not return to the scene.

I'm not sure how long they argued out in my driveway. I put on my PJs and went to sleep. The next morning, I found a positive pregnancy test in my mailbox. Telis sent eight dozen pink roses and a card that said something about new beginnings. He had his assistant deliver a gift every morning. Sunday, a diamond tennis bracelet. Monday, a pair of cross earrings. On Tuesday, she delivered a new high-end programmable coffee maker. I accepted all of his gifts with grace and forgiveness, but I never spoke to him again after that night. Don't judge me.

I changed churches because it was his church first. I left the city. It was his to love. Telis won the primary and lost the general. After that delightfully empowering experience, I ripped up my list and left my dating life to God.

Why am I telling you all of this? Because many women can't see God passed their broken hearts. This makes them bitter and stunts the growth of their faith. They build idols of men and romance. Otherwise wonderful women, get dragged into becoming mistresses, side chicks, and secret baby mamas to fill the holes in their hearts. The desire to be loved and cared for without the knowledge of God makes you vulnerable to being manipulated and taken advantage of. Been there. Done that. Got the t-shirt. I'm good.

Remember Adam, Eve, and that lying serpent in Genesis? The serpent exploited Eve's desire to be more and have more than what she already possessed. While she had much to be grateful for, she was more focused on what she didn't have. That sneaky 80/20 rule! You lose sight of the eighty percent you have, blinded by the twenty that you're missing. When it comes to relationships, love, and companionship, follow Matthew 6:33. Seek God above all else and the rest will be added to your life.

Selah.

ELEVEN

Our human hearts are fascinatingly fickle. We stand madly in love and pledge our lives "for better or worse" to the man or woman of our dreams. Tiny hearts dance in our eyes. If we're not holding our breath, the air that escapes us is insufficient for necessary oxygen exchange. It makes us light-headed and woozy. Many young girls dream of being brides from the first time they see Prince Charming kiss Snow White. When a woman selects her husband, he's her Prince Charming. When a man chooses his wife, he believes he has chosen the woman who will keep him interested and excited for the rest of his life. When those two people say I do they usually mean "I do at the moment."

The two well-intentioned people standing at the altar— "Prince Charming" and sexy, exciting "Forever Wife," think they have made the right choice for the life they desire. They have reasoned and rationalized. They have figured and fantasized. This is the person with whom they chose to do life. Sometimes that decision unravels within a year. Other times it takes decades. If I had a dollar for each time I've heard a married person say they were going to divorce when the kids leave home, I'd be writing this book from my house on Praslin. If I had a dollar for every time one of them actually did it, I might be able to buy a Popeye's chicken sandwich for lunch.

Divorce happens. I wish it didn't, but it does. From my experience, divorce is the ugliest of all failures. This is why I cannot understand those people who remain "good friends" after their divorce. Some couples even say that they became best friends after divorce. I don't get it. If you maintain enough respect for each other to become best friends, then can't you pull from that part of your heart to stay married? These BFF exes often celebrate holidays, take vacations, and hang out together. They do backyard barbecues and family reunions. While that might be the right thing to do for some, I'm not graced for it.

Marcos and I enjoy plenty of laughs when we're together at milestone events for Caden…graduations, birthdays, weddings, etc. When the event is over, we hug and go back to our separate lives. Our divorce was ugly and painful. I thank God we're passed it. It's encouraging that I can laugh and break bread with a man I actually hated at one point in my life. You know how the old saints say, "There's nothing between my soul and Jesus." Well, my disdain for Marcos was between my soul and Jesus back then.

Marcos and I didn't make it. Some people might believe it's because we were too young. I can give you ninety-nine reasons why our marriage failed, but age ain't one. I don't discourage young people who are led by God to marry. I know many people who got married very young and they are still together. I also know people who waited until they had established careers and thought they were ready. The marriage lasted as long as a June frost.

Another theory is that we were under too much financial pressure. I disagree. Our marriage didn't fall apart because we were broke. It fell apart because we were broken. I love marriage. I love being married. I believe that marriage is a marvelous gift beyond a beneficial social and economic institution. When you invite God into your marriage it can be an amazing tool for personal and spiritual growth, but marriage is hard work. The only people who think marriage is easy are people who just got married. I once heard a young woman boast, "Marriage is only work if you married the wrong person."

I had been married to Lenox twelve years at the time. I smirked and asked, "How long have you been married?"

"Almost two years," she beamed.

I smiled. "That's nice."

She's divorced now. She was married for fewer than five years.

Here's the deal... Eve was specifically created for Adam. She was bone of his bone and flesh of his flesh. Guess what? They still had conflict. It was major conflict with consequences that affect our marriages today. Marriage is made of two people with unique gifts and talents, with individual dreams and desires. These two people do life together, and there is no easy way to do it. Everything we have been blessed with requires work and care. Marriage is no different.

Lenox has warned me not to give you marital advice. I submit to his counsel. If you ask for advice on your marriage Lenox will say, "Ask God and I'll pray for you." He knows that what works for us might not work for you. In my opinion, marriage is eventually worth every day of it. In my experience, it doesn't get really dope until about ten years into the journey. I wish someone had told me this as a young wife. I think if seasoned married couples talked about their journeys, more young couples would get married and stay married.

Some people think you should divorce when you aren't happy. Some think you should divorce because God wants you to have peace. I can't help you make a decision about your marriage. However, I advise you not to make the decision lightly. Technically, that's not marital advice. It's advice on how to make decisions.

When Lenox and I were going through what I call "the storm of the century," I read an article that gave me pause. The article said that 86% of couples who didn't get a divorce when they wanted to, were happier and healthier five years later. It gave me hope. Now, I know it to be true. When people ask how Lenox and I have made it this far with all of the disruptions, distractions, disappointments, and negative marriage messages, I tell them this simple truth... "We never wanted to get a divorce at the same time." To God be the glory!

When I thought it was over, Lenox kept fighting. When he thought it was over, I kept fighting. We both kept praying until God aligned our hearts with His will for our marriage. That's it. That's all. It was #becauseJesus. So, to Lenox's point, I can't really give you any marital advice outside of "run to Jesus."

Here's what I will say about making decisions...

Don't make the decision to end your marriage emotionally. Don't make it while you are in a storm or in the bright sunshine. Both of these extremes affect your perspective. Storms and sunshine make it difficult to decide what God wants you to do. You must go beyond what you feel at the moment to discern God's wisdom in the situation. Marcos and I had sunny days that wrongly prolonged our season. Lenox and I had storms that almost took us out. Don't be pushed by the extremes. Stay balanced and stay in prayer. God will show you what to do.

My junior year of high school, my English teacher, Mrs. Drayton, assigned a poem for me to memorize. It's titled, "Oh, Oh You Will Be Sorry for That Word," a sonnet by Edna St. Vincent Millay. It begins with...

Oh, Oh, you will be sorry for that word!
Give back my book and take my kiss instead.
Was it my enemy or my friend I heard?
"What a big book for such a little head."

In hindsight, I clearly understand why Marcos and I divorced. I am able to articulate exactly why our marriage failed. I have the benefit of knowing what a great marriage looks like now. I have the emotional maturity to see beyond my feelings. I have the spiritual maturity to see the grace of God in my past. Although I could clean it up for you now, I won't. While I see it differently now, my journal clearly chronicled the reason for my divorce.

My marriage did not end because of the chaos and violence. It was not because of cheating, either. I assume that Marcos liked all of his girlfriends as much as I liked my boyfriend. We could have ended up being one of those couples that cheated on each other for fifty years. No. The reason for our divorce was written in my journal in all caps with a double underline.

"THIS NEGRO THINKS I'M A DAMN FOOL!"

Remember, Marcos and I were just kids, younger than twenty-five years old. Boys do not develop fully functional brains until their mid-to-late twenties. Until then, the ability to understand how ridiculous they sound is limited. To make a long story short...Marcos stayed out all night. He pulled up to a pile of wood in our driveaway. That pile was made of the deck spindles I had kicked out the night before. On top of the pile, our wedding photos, drenched in lighter fluid, were ready to be burned ala Angela Basset in Waiting to Exhale.

With birds chirping, Marcos walked through the door and Caden looked up at him. "Hi, Daddy. I couldn't find you."

"I was at the stadium, buddy." Marcos replied. "It's game day."

A five-year old knew better. "Did you sleep there?" Caden's brow raised. "You have on the same clothes as yesterday."

"Caden, eat your breakfast." I interjected before he could make an even bigger fool of his father.

I gave Marcos a wide-eyed look and warned him. "Don't say you were with Mitch because I spoke to him at one o'clock."

After a beat, Marcos found his answer. "I dropped Mitch off about twelve-thirty and stopped for gas. I was so tired I fell asleep at the pump."

Okay. Let's just go back to Edna St. Vincent Millay.

You will not catch me reading anymore.
I shall be called a wife to pattern by.
And some day when you knock and push the door,
Some sane day, not too bright and not too stormy,
I shall be gone, and you may whistle for me.

When I woke up the next day, St. Vincent-Millay's words were in my head. Reality set in for me. Marcos thought I was stupid enough to believe that he had fallen asleep at a gas pump and nobody woke him up for eight hours. It was time to go.

Caden and I lived with my girlfriend for a few weeks and then moved into an apartment. My decision was not made in haste. It wasn't made in a fit of emotional upheaval. Despite years of wild gestures and desperate wreckage, the day I left was a sane day. It was not too bright and not to stormy.

Two people navigating life together is a difficult proposition. Don't let anyone tell you otherwise. Don't let the highlight reels on Facebook and Instagram shape your opinion of what's real for you and your marriage. What your marriage looks like, feels like, and sounds like is between you, your spouse, and God. Do what works for the two of you. Do what works to keep your promise. Do what you said you would do when you said, "I do!"

I need to warn you of one last thing.

As I have said, I was certain of my decision to leave Marcos. There was nothing he could do to make me regret it…but he tried. About a year later, Marcos filed for full custody of Caden. He didn't win. But he did get physical custody for two reasons. The first is obvious. He was Marcos Gamble. The second was painfully factual. I had no support. I was all alone— in life, and more importantly, in that courtroom. Marcos' family showed up to court like it was a family reunion. Seriously, I think I saw his third cousin's wife's sister-in-law over there.

Marcos had his attorney, one of the top family lawyers in the city. I had a guy who thankfully wasn't a sports fan. Consequently, he wasn't terribly competitive either. The whole fiasco was an audacious attempt to break me and make me regret my decision. It made me regret ever marrying Marcos. It did not make me regret my divorce. In fact, it was confirmation that I had done the right thing.

Over the years, I spent thousands of dollars on better lawyers forcing Marcos to comply with our visitation orders. Finally, the judge threatened to hold Marcos in contempt if he ever saw me in his courtroom again. As many men know, battling over your visitation is a moral battle. By the time you get to court, Spring Break is over. Christmas is done. Your weekend has long passed. There is no real restitution other than your child knowing how much you love them.

While I've seen many dads give up and give in to manipulative baby mamas who use visitation to control them, I'm not a dad. I'm a mom. More accurately, I'm "mama" and I never give up on my boys.

Before you make the decision to end your marriage, be sure you aren't romanticizing what post-married life will be. If I had divorced Marcos for peace, I would have been sorely disappointed. He disrupted my peace for twelve more years. If I had decided to divorce Marcos for financial reasons, I'd would have been severely salted when he signed a max deal. While I'm not suggesting he only wanted custody of Caden to avoid paying child support, it was a noticeable benefit to the arrangement.

What happened to Marcos? He played a few more years in the league but didn't live up to the predictions. He eventually remarried. They divorced. He married again. That didn't work either. Marcos married a fourth time after he retired. This time I think Marcos has gotten it right. Lord, I pray he's gotten it right. Marcos has a beautiful family with a wife I absolutely adore. In fact, if I were graced to be BFFs with my past, I'd totally hang out with them.

No matter how pitiful or painful life got— and it certainly got painful— I have never regretted my decision to divorce Marcos. Without completely ignoring my husband's counsel, I want to give you this tiny piece of advice about marriage. Don't do it without God.

Rich, poor, sickness, health, better, or worse pretty much covers everything that can happen in a marriage. The decision to nullify that pledge is a difficult one. It takes prayer and counsel. If you're a Christian, it means alignment with God's word. Nobody can make the decision for you. I pray you have no condemnation if you get divorced. I pray you have unspeakable joy if you decide to stay married. In both cases, I pray God gives you peace that you don't even understand. That's what He has given me. Thanks be to God!

TWELVE

Now that you have some idea of who I am and what I've been through, you can better understand my time at New Jubilee Fellowship. While life itself is a great motivator of faith, we cannot disregard the role of the church. It builds, and sometimes breaks, the faith of God's people. I arrived at New Jubilee at a most critical time in my spiritual development. I was excited about all that I had discovered since that snowy day when I saw Jesus for the first time. I was curious and hungry to develop true Christian faith beyond simply going to church.

This is a very fragile place on the journey to deep faith. Honestly, it's the place where your faith can blossom. It's also the place where things can go terribly wrong. This is the time in the faith walk where many people move from Bible-based Christianity into mystical, hocus pocus religion. They know enough to be dangerous to themselves, and not enough to be even remotely effective against the devil. That's where I was when I arrived at NJF.

Recovering from my childhood was a daily effort for many years. Meeting Jesus was just the beginning of my healing. When I arrived at New Jubilee Fellowship, I still had plenty of hangover abandonment issues from my parents, my marriage, and our ugly custody war.

I had a tremendous amount of reverence and respect for Bishop Gilliam and Lady G, the founders of the church. I trusted them completely and hung on to every word of their teaching. While I would not define my time at New Jubilee as a positive experience in my life, I certainly characterize it as powerfully productive in the formation of my faith.

I arrived at New Jubilee as a smart, beautiful, well-paid, tithing young woman. This moved me to the front of the line in congregational importance. It also piqued the curiosity of Bishop and Lady G. Like most churches, the congregation of New Jubilee was filled with broken people. Because it was a "young" church, boasting nearly half of its membership under the age of thirty, there were plenty of women and men who were not too far removed from the physical, emotional, or sexual abuses of their childhoods. It was a congregation of severely broken people, and I had found my tribe.

New Jubilee Church was non-denominational. That means that Bishop Gilliam was the end-all and be-all when it came to all things. All opinions, assertions, and authority stopped at him. It was a dangerous situation, but I did not know it at the time. Up to that point, I had only attended small Baptist churches that were part of a larger governing body.

Before we go any further, I need to tell you something. There are some bad churches out there. Be careful. There are some bad ministers who don't believe the words coming from their mouths on Sunday morning. When it comes to ministry, there are a bushel of bad apples spoiling the good fruit. However, not all churches cheat. Not all pastors lie. Pastors are human and they have flaws. Churches, like Noah's ark, can get a little funky. For every two peaceful doves, there are two stubborn asses. While the pastor and the people are sometimes janky, Jesus is not.

Turn to your neighbor and say, "Jesus is never janky." Be sure you don't hold Jesus accountable for the faults of his people. People are flawed. Jesus is not. People are flaky. Jesus is not. Okay, moving on...

New Jubilee Church was a good church as far as I could tell when I arrived. The teaching was from the Bible not personal revelation. There wasn't any unreasonable financial pressure on the congregation beyond the encouragement to tithe. Bishop Gilliam was sometimes criticized in the media and characterized as being predatory for having a church in the hood and a house in the suburbs. That was no big deal to me. Non-Christians believe that any level of material success associated with the church is wrong. They haven't read the Bible.

Bishop Gilliam collected a salary commensurate with pastoring a church of such size. The Bible says that the love of money leads to all kinds of harmful behavior and consequences. Check out 1 Timothy 6:10. It also says that God can bless you with wealth without all the hijinks. That's Proverbs 10:22. The bottom line is this. Don't do ungodly things to get money or to hold on to money. You can be a rich Christian. In fact, being a broke Christian likely means you are not following Christian principles of stewardship, generosity, and debt management. You shouldn't be a broke

Christian. At any rate, Bishop Gilliam was doing alright for himself, but nothing outrageous.

My life at the church was incestuous. All of my friends were from New Jubilee. We had a whole squad of sanctified dimes and spiritual stunners. My hairdresser, nail technician, dentist, and doctor were all members of New Jubilee. I didn't interact with anyone who wasn't a member. New Jubilee became my work and my life. There was no balance. In hindsight, I can clearly see it was a cult. Or maybe it was simply cult-ish.

Soon after I arrived at New Jubilee, I formally joined the church. It's how I was raised. Up to that point I had been a good Baptist girl who memorized the church covenant. "We moreover engage that, when we remove from this place, we will as soon as possible unite with some other church where we can carry out the spirit of this covenant and the principles of God's word." So, after three or four Sundays I walked the aisle.

Upon joining, I was quickly given a spiritual gifts test. This is an assessment to determine what talents and abilities God has given you. These talents and abilities are given to you to help and serve others. I've been given the gifts of leadership, mercy, discernment, evangelism, teaching, and knowledge. They usually only focus on the top three gifts, but I had a perfect score on all six of these. Faith, healing, exhortation, and prophecy were all only one or two points short of a perfect score. Most important to Bishop Gilliam was that I scored very low in the gifts of helps and administration. It basically means I'm an intuitive visionary leader who doesn't concern myself with the details. Oh…and if I like something a lot, I'm going to tell you about it.

I sat across the massive mahogany desk from Bishop Gilliam. His chair was quite ornate. Though it had no gold, rubies, or emeralds, it was unmistakably designed to be a throne. New Jubilee Fellowship was his kingdom. It was a well-established principle during new member training. His photo hung in the classrooms next to Jesus so the children would understand who was in charge. Jesus was the perfect, human version of God. Bishop Gilliam was the nearly perfect, human version of Jesus. Seriously… that's how one Sunday school teacher explained it to the children.

Bishop looked over my test results. He made a few "mmmm hmmm" and smiled. I knew he was pleased. "You're no minion," he said. "You'll be with us."

Bishop's words were melodious. Since the day Kayla put me on blast for not being a real member of the Sparks family, it was all I ever wanted...somewhere to belong. More importantly, I wanted to be somewhere where I felt like I belonged.

Being the leader is not the same as belonging. In fact, it is usually the opposite of belonging. It's lonely and isolated. You never find what you're looking for until you create it. New Jubilee was the place I had been seeking and I didn't have to create it. These were my people. Like I said, this was my tribe.

I sought love. I sought acceptance. I sought good ol' fashioned kindness. Let me stop right here and tell you why it ended badly. Matthew 6:33 says to seek first the kingdom of God and his righteousness, and everything else will follow. I had it backwards with New Jubilee. I was looking for a place in this world to find God. When in fact, I should have been seeking God to find my place in this world.

Many congregants at New Jubilee often confused me as being one of Bishop Gilliam's children. He and Lady G has two sons and seven daughters. After my spiritual gifts test, Bishop Gilliam assigned his youngest daughter, Andi, as my accountability partner. Andi and I were born on the same day in the same year. As you might recall, I was born at 5:55 in the morning. Andi was born at 6:42 in the evening. We joked that I was the older sister. Some people even thought we were twins.

I was in line at Ben & Jerry's the first time I realized that this mixup was going to be a problem for me. Pressure mounted as I moved closer to the front of the line, unable to decide between Cherry Garcia and Chunky Monkey. A young woman with green contacts and an extra bundle of blonde in her ponytail sped towards me. I took a step backward as she invaded my personal space with nails that curved downward to the floor. She pointed at me.

"You're one of Bishop's daughters," she said in a way that made me think she was going to rob me.

It always annoyed me the way people simply called Bishop Gilliam, "Bishop," as if he were the only bishop in town. We all know there is only one bishop in America famous enough to be called by a single name. I don't even have to tell you who it is. You know who I'm talking about, don't you?

I smiled politely. "No, I'm not one of Bishop Gilliam's daughters."

"You're not?" She asked again as if I were lying.

"No."

"Well, you're super light-skinned and you preach so I thought you was." Indignant, she stomped to the back of the line like her mistake was my fault.

As I moved closer to the front of the line and the pressure mounted on my decision, I felt a tap on my shoulder. The woman behind me was a member of New Jubilee, as well. She leaned in and whispered. "You got too much power and authority to be one of Bishop's daughters."

I smiled. No teeth.

An older gentleman in front of me turned around. "She's telling the truth young lady. God's going to do big things with you for the kingdom." He was a member of NJF, too.

This was the moment I realize that there was no escape from New Jubilee Fellowship members. They were everywhere. They knew me. I didn't know them. I was at a clear disadvantage. When I got to the front of the line and ordered my ice cream the clerk said, "No charge. That man paid for it."

I turned around and the older gentleman stood at the door. He lifted his ice cream cone in a toast. "I appreciate you pastor," he said.

I nearly dropped my ice cream. "I'm not a p—"

The bell on the door rang and he was gone before I could correct him. The woman behind me put her hand on my shoulder. "Shhh don't claim that."

I turned to her, terribly annoyed that she was touching me. "Claim what?" I snapped.

"Don't claim that you're not a pastor," she warned.

New Jubilee Church was known as a charismatic church. It was a "name it and claim it" church. The movement, while wildly popular, puzzled me. In the springtime, my eyes water. My nose runs. I sometimes sneeze more than twenty times in row. I have allergies. I usually start my allergy medication at the end of February to avoid being attacked by the pollen drop of the approaching floral spring. As a member of New Jubilee, I was told not to claim my allergies.

One day I sneezed during bible study. Now, if you have ever been in a church with any Pentecostal influence, you know that a sneeze can set off an entire clamor. If you sneeze at the wrong time, people will think you have a demon. If you sneeze at the right time...actually, there is no right time to sneeze in a Pentecostal church. It makes things stressfully awkward during allergy season.

"Pray about it," Deacon Wood advised me.

"About what?" I asked.

"Your allergies."

"But you told me not to claim it," I said.

He nodded. "That's right."

"If I don't claim it, how can I pray about it? Don't I have to say that I'm sick in order to be healed?" I asked.

I was not being facetious. I wasn't trying to be a smarty pants. It was a real question. I didn't understand how I could seek healing for something that I wouldn't claim. Remember, I was a Baptist girl. I wasn't taught about all this naming and claiming stuff.

Deacon Wood was forty years my senior. He didn't need to explain anything to me, so he furrowed his brow and dipped his chin. "I said, pray about it."

So, I did. I also studied my Bible. Here's what I found. Everybody who came to Jesus for healing acknowledged that they were sick. The bleeding woman in Mark 5 did not ignore her situation. If so, she would have never pressed her way to Jesus for healing. She wasn't going to sit there and bleed to death thinking, "I'm not claiming it."

I don't see anywhere in the Bible where "don't claim it" is a thing, particularly when it comes to the reality of life. If we could simply not claim things to rid our lives of them, then let's not claim COVID and cancer. Let's not claim child abuse and school shooters. Listen, I would never do another plank if I could just "not claim" my mommy tummy. Instead, I am forced to do crunches and swear off carbs for life.

I completely objected to name it and claim it theology. People were taking it too far. New Jubilee members were "not claiming" Biblical principles if they didn't fit their lifestyle choices. I was on the ministry team with a young woman named Delilah. I know…but that was really her name. We called her "Dee" for obvious reasons. She had been sleeping with a man named Antoine for over a year. His wife went to the altar every Sunday and wailed in prayer.

Sometimes, she'd go without an altar call. She'd fall to her knees and sob.

One day after I couldn't take it anymore, I told Dee that she was wrong. To my surprise, she responded confidently. "I don't claim that condemnation. Don't put your convictions on me."

"This isn't my conviction. It's right here." I held my Bible in the air.

"I claim Antoine as my husband," Dee boasted.

"You're tripping." I threw my hands up and headed back to my desk. "I'm just going to pray for you."

"You need to pray for his wife," Delilah spouted.

I turned back towards her with an intense stare. "Oh, don't worry. I will."

"Naming and claiming" is one of those hocus pocus things that gets people off track and sometimes causes them to lose faith. That's what happened to Delilah. Antoine refused to divorce his wife. After a few months of me agreeing with his wife in prayer, Antoine broke off his relationship with Delilah. He decided he needed to fully commit to his faith…and to his wife.

Antoine and his wife moved to a new church a few blocks away. Delilah's pain drove her to drugs and alcohol. In her mind, Jesus had failed to give her what she claimed— somebody else's husband. She left the church…and Jesus.

Under the falsehood of "name it and claim it" faith, people claimed houses they couldn't afford. Within two years, they were in foreclosure. To land jobs they weren't qualified for, they claimed skills and experience they didn't actually have. Soon after, they found themselves claiming unemployment. New Jubilee Fellowship was a name it and claim it circus, and I was in the center ring.

THIRTEEN

My work at New Jubilee blossomed and my faith had grown deeper than I could have ever imagined. While I struggled with the people in the building and some of their antics, I had been able to do some really good work. This was extremely beneficial for my healing. I learned two big lessons during my time at New Jubilee Fellowship.

While our protective inclination is to be self-serving and insulated, we were created by God to serve and love others. It actually feels good to help other people when you are in pain. This was a surprising discovery for me. However, I also learned that you cannot heal yourself by loving and serving others. Eventually you'll have to face the pain and love yourself just as much.

After a year of training, Bishop Gilliam made Andi and me co-leads for Teen youth ministry. This didn't help much with the confusion around me being one of the Gilliam girls. I was the only person in leadership who wasn't in the family. The Gilliam's oldest daughter, Joanna, was married. Her husband was the assistant pastor of the church on paper, while she did all the work. Bishop Gilliam's two nephews served as associate pastors with his two sons, but none of them could preach. With nine children and two nephews, Bishop Gilliam couldn't find a preacher in the bunch. I suppose that's why he called me his eighth daughter, "a new beginning" he'd say with a gleam in his eyes.

Andi and I created a Friday night service that sometimes had over five-hundred teenagers in church. It was astounding. Andi led praise and worship, and I preached. We got along very well, initially. But that was short lived.

I quickly came to question Andi's sincerity in matters of faith. I wasn't so sure she had ever experienced Jesus for herself. While the older Gilliam children weren't called to preach, they certainly displayed a genuine love for the Lord. Andi was the youngest of the Gilliam gang. Unlike her siblings, she had been born into a thriving ministry and considered herself "called" from birth. For Andi, New

Jubilee was the family business. It was to remain profitable so that her family could remain powerful.

When drama surfaced, you could be sure Andi's name was somewhere in it. She was toxic and destructive to the young congregation. She developed a clique of mean girls called, "The A Team," who were her disciples. I uncovered that Andi was collecting a personal offering from these girls weekly. Andi told these young women that they were handpicked by her and God. The A-team were gossipy, mean-spirited girls who did not embrace the Christian values we aimed to teach them. At least, not the ones I aimed to teach.

I discussed the A-team with Andi a number of times. She refused to correct them and continued to incite their behavior. Andi and the A-team threw soda into the face of a young woman who refused to join them. They spread rumors about people they didn't like. They made fun of the way people dressed and the way they walked. They even made fun of the way I talked with my proud Appalachian drawl.

Andi once pulled a sixteen-year-old, pregnant girl to the front of the church. "Tell them your name," she barked.

The girl lowered her eyes. "Tabby."

Andi placed both hands on Tabby's round belly and said, "This child is formed in sin from lust. She will be molested by the time she's ten years old and used as an instrument of lust."

Tabby shrieked in fear and burst into tears. The A-team giggled and pointed at Tabby. Andi spouted rhythmic syllables that were supposed to sound spiritual but sounded more like utter gibberish. She "bobo tata nana" herself into a frenzy. The other teens were mortified. The whole service was disrupted. That was it. Andi had left me no choice but to go to her father.

Bishop Gilliam was outraged by Andi's behavior. He scolded me for not coming to him sooner about the A-team. Bishop Gilliam didn't just stop Andi from leading praise and worship, he forbade her to come to church for seven weeks.

After meeting with the members of the A-team individually, Bishop Gilliam asked the girls and their parents to leave the church. Honestly, I felt like this reaction was a little excessive. It baffled me. A month later, I discover that Andi had been sent to conversion therapy for those seven weeks. She was a lesbian. I was unsure if they could change her sexuality, but I prayed they would change her nasty disposition. They didn't.

Andi was still gay when she came home from conversion therapy…and meaner than ever. She hated me for telling her father about the A-team. While mothers marched their sons in front of her Sunday after Sunday, Andi pretended to be "super picky" and refuse them. I watched Bishop and Lady G navigate the situation with grace. It wasn't my business and I stayed focused on ministry. Things were going well.

Have you ever noticed how we say, "this too shall pass" when things are going badly, but never consider it when things are going right? Well, let me tell you something. When things are going well in your life, praise God. When you have moments of peace and contentment, take the time to thank God because "this too shall pass."

My faith had grown stronger than ever. I was no longer just a church girl but had developed true faith in Jesus. Most importantly, I was finally starting to believe that God loved me. I was starting to make sense of my past and I came to understand that all of it could be used for God's glory and the good of others. I was on fire for Jesus and I didn't care who knew it. So, you know what that means? It means trouble. I was headed for trouble and had no idea.

It was a chilly Saturday morning that promised to be a beautiful spring day. My good friend Sasha and I started our spring exercise routine. We hoped it would be the one that would rid us of those winter pounds the scale lies about. We took a spirited three-mile walk around the pond in our newly purchased sneakers and exercise gear. We were cute if nothing else. This was the year that we'd stick to our goal.

Sasha was a member of New Jubilee Fellowship, of course. I didn't have any friends who weren't members. Sasha and her husband were deacons. We had other things in common, too. We both had painful childhoods and were estranged from women we considered to be terrible mothers. We both married the wrong person in college and were divorced from those volatile relationships.

Sasha was five or six years older than me and had already married again. Her husband was a wonderful man who loved her with passion and insight. God had blessed her. It gave me hope for what might be next for me.

After the walk, we decided to reward ourselves with a down home breakfast. The calories we burned off were waiting for us when we arrived at "Sister," a popular soul food restaurant that was ironically owned by four brothers who never had a sister. We were forced to wait outside until a table opened. The smell of biscuits and gravy, fried chicken, and dark roasted coffee sabotaged our morning efforts around the pond. We didn't care. A meal at Sister was always worth it.

Once we were seated, we struggled to hear each other in conversation. It was a down home soul food restaurant full of Black people and Puerto Ricans. Everybody's inside voice was better suited for outside. We discussed the upcoming church revival. A popular television minister, Bishop Donner, was coming to town as a guest preacher. I was excited. Sasha, not so much.

"He's a prophaliar! I can't stand him," Sasha spewed across the table. I was taken aback. While I had always known Sasha to be rough and reckless with her words, I had never heard her speak ill of church people. She was bitter, without a doubt. We all knew that. However, when Sasha loved someone or something, she was the gentlest, kindest, most generous heart anyone could find. I was delighted to be one of the "someones" she loved.

Apparently, Sasha met Bishop Donner shortly after she married her wonderful husband. They were trying to get pregnant at the time. Bishop Donner laid hands on her and declared that she would have daughters and sons.

"He told me I would have children. He's a liar and a fake."

"Okay, but that doesn't mean he lied. You haven't had children yet," I said.

Sasha continued to hurl insults about Bishop Donner. This was before social media. I have no idea how she knew so many things about his personal life, but Sasha was convinced that he was a hypocritical charlatan. She was angry with Bishop Donner. She was angry with Bishop Gilliam for bringing Bishop Donner to our church. Most obviously, Sasha was angry with God that she couldn't get pregnant.

"God gave her a daughter and she didn't deserve it." She said, referencing her mother.

"He hasn't given you one yet," I emphasized. I was probably a little too loud.

Sasha was angry but she was also afraid of motherhood. She didn't say it, but I knew it. Remember, I have mercy, discernment, and wisdom as spiritual gifts. I felt her fear in my body and the Holy Spirit showed me why she was afraid.

My life was far from perfect even in that moment, but I defended God. Sasha and I had similar backgrounds and similar pain. I knew the anger and fear that suffocated her. Overly focused on her appearance and showing off an obnoxious collection of luxury shoes and exotic vacations, she was as broken as anyone of us could be. To be honest, I wasn't too different from her at the time. I suppose that's why we became close friends.

"The doctors said I could not have children, but I had Caden. He's a miracle."

She rolled her eyes. "And look at that situation," she said.

Ouch! That hurt, but I had to push through my own pain to help her.

"Yep." I quoted a popular song at the time. "It's funny how money changes a situation."

I was on a roll. While Sasha knew much of my story already, I decided to tell her the vivid details of my abuse — which I haven't even told you yet. I told her how my body was broken because of what they did to me. In the moment,

I would have described myself as being passionate to the point of losing myself. Now, I know that it was the Holy Spirit.

I told her about my abandonment, abuse, brokenness, and shame. I told her about when my parents found blood in my toddler underwear and ignored it. I told her how I lied when they asked me if something had happened to me and they were so stupid, selfish, or coked out that they couldn't discern the truth from a four-year old. I told her that they never took me to the doctor to see where that blood was from. They didn't stop sending me to that house to be abused over and over and over again. I told Sasha how six young men took turns smothering my preschool body in their sweat and semen gouging my insides and asking me if I was woman enough to take it.

"But here I am. God is good. ALL THE DAMN TIME!" I thundered from the depth of my soul.

I had lost myself in the conversation. I reached my hand across the table and asked her if she was afraid to be a mother. She admitted that she was. Sasha never knew her father, not even his name. But apparently, she looked like him. Her mother abused her emotionally and physically because of it. Sasha was afraid that she would abuse her own children because she was abused. I told her that the devil was using that fear to block her pregnancy. Then I prayed for her. Again, I must have been quite loud.

At the end of the prayer, I noticed the clamorous restaurant had gone quiet. I looked around and everyone was staring at me. There were a few tables of people with their hands in the air praising God. Tears and sniffles had replaced the laughter and raucous conversation. When we sat down nobody was at the table next to us. Now, there was a man at the adjacent table. I didn't see him come in. Neither did Sasha. I don't know his name, but let's call him Gabe.

Gabe was a brown-skin man with a rugged gray beard and head full of hair. I imagine that he was somebody's grandpa enjoying breakfast, except he hadn't ordered anything. There were no plates or cups on this table. Tears streamed from his face. Now, I was totally embarrassed.

Gabe pointed his finger at me and said, "They say the harvest is ripe and the laborers are few, but they haven't seen you yet." He shook his finger and locked eyes with me. "Oh, when they see you."

The quiet tears and sniffles of the restaurant had been replaced with sobs and shouts of "Hallelujah!" A full-blown praise broke out in the restaurant. Praises in English and Spanish filled the room. "Oh, El Senor!" I was overwhelmed. I was astounded. I was spooked as I looked into the kitchen and saw the chef on his knees praying.

I never went back to Sister after that day. Gabe's words rang in my head day and night. My preaching got bolder and more authentic. I wasn't afraid to teach and preach the word of God as it stood. Bishop Gilliam woke up one Sunday and said the Lord told him to have me preach Sunday morning service. That same morning, I woke up with a message in my heart. Bishop Gilliam gave me a five-thousand-dollar love offering after I preached that day.

"Obedience to God comes with rewards," he said.

Lady G shouted all over the church that Sunday because I preached from Isaiah 30:20, "Although the Lord gives you the bread of adversity and the water of affliction, your teachers will be hidden no more; with your own eyes you will see them."

A few months later my friend Sasha and her wonderful husband got pregnant. She had a beautiful baby girl. She eventually had four children, two daughters and two sons. Bishop Donner is a prophet.

While Gabe's word sparked a fire in my heart and things were going well, trouble was brewing. But like I said... God is good. All the damn time.

FOURTEEN

While I remained focused on introducing the teens to Jesus, Andi continued her reign of terror. She established a new group of mean girls, 20-somethings. She had a boyfriend and they held hands in church on Sunday. She was miserable. Therefore, determined to make everyone else miserable too.

Her primary target was me, and I had been warned by more than a few people to watch my back. Andi and I didn't even pretend to get along anymore. We stopped speaking completely. During Friday service, she led praise and worship and left the sanctuary when I got up to preach.

It was the perfect day for a church cookout, not too hot and plenty of sunshine. Kirk Franklin blasted from oversized speakers. While the older members grimaced and frowned at the music, they were outnumbered by us, the under forty crowd. I wore my green "Only Jesus" t-shirt, a denim mini skirt, and pink Chuck Taylors.

Sasha and I were dressed alike. She wore the same t-shirt but with green designer sneakers and a denim skirt that cost more than my whole outfit, including my overpriced Victoria Secret bra. She had dropped all of her baby weight and looked amazing for having a four-month-old. When we arrived, her husband was on the grill with the other deacons. His eyes shined with honor as he watched Sasha push the stroller across the field.

While I aimed to enjoy myself at the cookout, being on the staff meant the cookout was a work function. So, rather than being a day off, I spent the time praying for people.

"Pastor…" I heard a voice behind me.

I looked up from my plate to find "Pretty Pam." I called her Pretty Pam because there were two very active Pams at the church. I called the other one, "Cutie Pam."

"Pretty Pam, what's up?" I asked.

"Pastor, pray for me." I gave her a look and she corrected herself. "Sister T, I need you to pray that I get a new job. Those folks are weighing on my spirit."

I immediately grabbed Pretty Pam's hands to pray. "If your situation requires you to interrupt my fried whiting sandwich, then we're going to pray right now."

I'm that chick. If you ask for prayer, I pray right then and right where we are. Bishop Gilliam taught me that. He said we teach people how to pray for themselves by praying with them, not just for them. I had just finished praying with the kids who were going off to college in a few weeks when I saw Sasha dash across the grass. She pushed the baby stroller like she was fleeing a house fire. Her face matched the intensity of her stride.

"Sasha!" I called out.

She waved me off.

I ran after her. "What's wrong?"

She was in tears. "Just forget it."

"Forget what?"

"They are pure evil. All of them."

I didn't need to ask who. I already knew. I jumped in front of the stroller to block Sasha's path. Briefly distracted by the cuteness of her daughter, also dressed in pink and green, I demanded she tell me what happened. She did. As usual, Andi had insulted Sasha. Even worse, she insulted the baby.

When Sasha told me what they said, I snapped. I stormed across the grass and walked straight up to Andi and her crew.

"You wicked brood of vipers," I snarled, using the insult Jesus used on the Pharisees in the Gospel of Matthew. I was over the top back then like a younger version of Aunt Esther from Sanford and Son. "You know her struggles, Andi. Why would you say she's a bad mother?"

One of the minions spouted, "Because she is…putting that baby in those demonic colors."

I took a deep breath and guess what I did… I walked away. I turned around and walked away. That was when Andi shouted at me. "Jezebel! In that hot pink lipstick and short skirt."

Are you holding your breath? Because I did. I counted to five. Then, went to ten. It didn't work. Before I knew it, I stormed back and got right in Andi's face. "You like it, don't you?"

There was a collective gasp from the circle. I shooed them away before I continued. "Get to steppin'!"

The crew scattered in opposing directions like sand being released from a magnet. This was it. I was nose-to-nose with Andi like a Fight Night poster.

"You can't focus with pretty girls around? You've got to run Sasha away because she's too cute." I taunted her. "That new boyfriend of yours isn't holding your attention. Is he?"

The woman who boldly prayed that day in "Sister" was unfamiliar to me. The powerful woman Gabe spoke of, she scared me. I didn't know her. This woman, the one telling off Andi at the church cookout— I knew exactly who she was. She was Toyi Elizabeth.

Andi's lip quivered. I leaned into her and growled through clenched teeth, a fake smile of sorts. "If I didn't love your father, I'd put you on blast out here. You're a disgrace. Not because you're gay. But because you're an evil, godless, bully pharisee. "

I told you I was like Aunt Esther. I just needed the tambourine.

Nobody heard what I said, but plenty of people saw us. The deacons on the grill watched intensely. Bishop Gilliam and Lady G were busy being good hosts while several of the older members looked on from a distance, including the man who bought my ice cream that day. He blocked the view of Lady G so she couldn't see us. I saw him do it. I knew he did it was on purpose. I think the whole church secretly wanted Andi to finally get hers.

The next morning, my phone rang three minutes before my alarm was set to go off. "Hello."

It was Lady G.

"I would like to meet with you after church," she said.

I paused before I responded. "Do you want to meet with me as First Lady or as Andi's mother?"

"Does it make a difference?" she asked.

"If you want to meet with me as First Lady, then I'll gladly come. If this is about my disagreement with Andi," I let the silence sit for a beat. "Andi and I are grown. You can't fight her battles."

Lady G changed her tone to one more conducive to getting what she wanted. "As First Lady, I would counsel you on this conflict whether it was with my daughter or not. There was a better way to handle Andi's behavior...and I've dealt with her behavior. She has apologized to Deacon Sasha and Deacon Rick."

That softened me up a bit. "Okay. I'll meet with you."

"Great. Come to my office after service."

I hung up the phone and jumped in the shower.

When I arrived at church, Lady G greeted me with a tight hug. "I still love you."

"I love you, too," I said.

"Andi can be a handful and I appreciate the grace you've given her," she said.

"Andi and I are adults. You don't need to insert yourself in this, Lady G."

Most first ladies are sweet and demure on the outside and full of resentment and insecurity on the inside. Lady G was no different. "Oh, I won't," she said with the kind of passive aggression only a preacher's wife could muster.

While I knew Andi and I were going to battle, I never could have imagined what happened next.

After church I went to Lady G's office. Her secretary told me that she was down in the small conference room. That was a lie.

I walked down the hall to the conference room. When I entered, I was stunned by what I saw. Bishop Gilliam sat at the head of the table with his two sons, two nephews, and several male deacons, including Deacon Wood. Twelve men with scowls on their faces waited for me. A few, with fangs showing.

"Sit down," Bishop Gilliam barked.

As a woman who had been sexually abused as a child and then physically and emotionally abused by men most of my life at that time, my vulnerability overtook me. My heartbeat was deafening and the lump in my throat was bigger than the knot in my stomach. I must have looked quite pitiful because one son changed his scowl to kind eyes.

"Who told you?" Bishop Gilliam asked. "Who was it?"

I swallowed the lump in my throat and the knot in my stomach got twice as big. "The Holy Spirit."

Deacon Wood sprung from his seat. "That's it. I'm out of here."

"Jerry, wait!" Bishop Gilliam croaked.

"No Phillip." Deacon Wood held firm. "The girl said the Holy Spirit told her. I'm done."

Deacon Wood left the meeting with his hands in the air. I was uncomfortable and very afraid.

Bishop Gilliam pulled out his Bible. He turned to Proverbs 5 and began to read. It was the first time I had ever seen him start a meeting without prayer. "For the lips of the immoral woman drip honey, and her speech is smoother than oil, but in the end, she is bitter as gall..."

As he read, tears drained down my face. I could feel my eyes swell with each word. His eldest son, the kind one, gave me a tissue. You'll have to read the whole thing to get an idea of how devastated I was. I was sobbing by the time he finished.

When he finished reading, he said, "This is you."

Since the day I met Bishop Gilliam, I believed every word that came from his mouth came from God. So, God was calling me a whore though I had not had sex in over three years at the time.

I gasped for air and spoke through broken sobs, "This is not me."

"It is! Even your worship is seductive." Bishop Gilliam slammed his hand on the table. "You come in here, infecting the minds of men and women. You have entered the dreams of every man in this room and seduced us."

"What?!" I was confused. I felt the pieces of my soul break off and drop to the floor like a shattered vase.

I was physically raped for the first time when I was three years old. For nearly five years those men abused me regularly. Bobby Spark's family raped me physically. Bishop Gilliam and his people raped me spiritually.

Barely able to breathe, I asked a very important question. And that's when God's grace strengthened me. "Bishop, have you prayed about this? Did God say this about me?"

He threw his Bible across the room. "Some things I don't need to pray about."

At first, I didn't recognize the man who was saying those terrible things about me. Then I realized it was Andi's father. He wasn't being led by God. He wasn't being my pastor.

Prayer was the cornerstone of everything Bishop Gilliam taught us. We prayed multiple times a service. We prayed before meals and prayed prayers of thanksgiving after meals. Bishop Gilliam prayed more than any man I had ever known. Yet, in this moment he admitted — either consciously or not, that he had not prayed about this situation. He had not heard from God.

With this revelation I reached for a tissue. The son with the kind eyes pushed the box toward me with a guilty, but remorseful expression. It was the culpable visage you offer homeless people when you drive by them with an ashtray full of toll money.

"We called Marcos Gamble," Bishop Gilliam said, hoping to produce more tears.

"What?" I asked. The knot in my stomach flopped. Marcos and I despised each other after the divorce.

"He speaks very highly of you," the kind son interjected before my mind could get too carried away. That was God!

"Why did you lose your son?" one deacon asked.

"I didn't lose my son," I said. "What are you talking about?"

"Marcos said he took him from you because you were unfit," Bishop charged.

"He did not!" The kind son shouted. But he backed down when his father glared at him.

"He said you were an awful mother who abandoned your son. What kind of mother does that? Who is your mother? Where is your mother? You've been here for years and you haven't had one family member visit you."

"I...I don't have a family." My tears returned.

"Everybody has a family," another deacon said with a fist pounding the table.

"I don't!" I pounded my fist right back. I wasn't afraid anymore. I had been transplanted back to my childhood, back to my marriage. It was time to fight. I knew how to fight and cry at the same time.

Bishop Gilliam leaned into me. "How do you explain this? You have no family. You're already divorced at such a young age. Your child was taken from you. You whisk in here like a hurricane and muddy my ministry."

"I did no such thing! You brought me in after my gifts test."

"You're a witch!" He shouted.

"I am not!"

"You're a harlot!" he barked.

"I am not!"

"Dad Stop!" the kind son begged.

I stood to my feet and wiped my eyes again. "If you want me to leave your church just say that. If you don't want me here because I know about Andi, then you could have just said that. Kick me out like you did the A-team, but don't create a narrative that makes you feel better about it."

Bishop Gilliam sat back in his chair.

One of the nephews stood to his feet to loom over me. "You say you're not a harlot. How many men have you had sex with?"

Another nephew piled on, "What positions do you have sex in?"

I looked around the room and they were nearly foaming at the mouth for verbal porn. They wanted to rape me, just like the men from my childhood. They wanted to break me, like Marcos and his family. There was only one problem with that... This time, I knew Jesus.

I ignored them as they peppered inappropriately graphic questions at me. One of them grabbed my hand and placed it on his erection. "Look what you do to us."

I snatched my hand away and burst into tears again. "Get behind me Satan!"

This was getting out of hand. Bishop Gilliam's face had lost its color. The fire of vengeance in his eyes had diminished to embers. I looked him square in his face as if he were on my level...because he was. The pedestal I built for him had been shattered. He was just a man. A man who was angry that his daughter was gay and needed someone to take it out on since he couldn't punch God in the face.

"You better thank God that I know Jesus. I'm leaving this church and taking my blessing with me."

A tear finally escaped Bishop Gillian's eye. "You can run if you want to," he barked.

I turned back to him. "I'm walking."

The kind son got up from his seat and open the door for me. I nodded and said thank you.

Despite the amazing display of courage and strength in the room with those men, I spent the next three days in bed in unspeakable pain. I didn't eat. I didn't sleep, that I can recall. I laid there, lifeless, just as I used to do as a little girl with grown men on top of me. I had been gouged, soiled, and spiritually broken. That's how I ended up in the room full of heroes dressed in Carolina blue, trying to save my life.

FIFTEEN

Suicide is a spirit, one with which I am intimately familiar. The first time I wanted to die was I eight years old. I was fourteen when I realized that I could make it happen. In the early 80s a young woman named Elizabeth Bouvia checked into a psychiatric hospital in Los Angeles with a request to be allowed to starve to death. She was almost completely paralyzed and was in tremendous physical and emotional pain. Her story sparked a "right to die" movement.

I'm not sure how I came across this information as a teenager without the ubiquity of the internet, but I did. I wrote a research paper on Euthanasia and decided to put myself out of my misery. It was the summer before high school. I had been carrying the burden of abuse for eleven years, basically my whole life.

Back then, I worked at a bookstore a mile from our home. Perhaps that's where I discovered Bouvia's story. As a dancer, I'd balance myself gracefully on the curb and walk to work mostly on my toes. On this particular day, I decided to throw myself in front of moving car. It was my right to die.

In my fourteen-year-old mind, God had designed my life to be full of pain and disappointment. So, I would cut that story short by dying young. It never occurred to me how devastated my family and friends would be if I died.

Before I left the house, I gave my eleven-year-old brother a big hug and told him how much I loved him. He said "Yuck!" and I laughed. I walked out the front door and looked up at the sky where there was only a single fluff in view. My great grandmother used to say that if there was enough blue in the sky to make a Dutchman a pair of britches, it would be a good day. This was sure to be the happiest day of my life. I trotted down the front stairs and whirled out to the curb, delighted that my pain would soon be over. I balanced on my toes with an occasional spin and a smile and waited for the roar of a car behind me. I had it all planned out.

The bookstore was located twelve blocks from my house on the busiest street in town. Each day as I walked to work, my intimate thoughts were interrupted by a honking horn or a shout from a schoolmate hanging out of a passenger side window. Most times someone stopped to offer me a ride, but I always declined because those long walks to work were the most peaceful moments of my life. On this day, I decided to wait until the halfway point of my journey to enact my plan. I didn't want to be close enough to home that my little brother might see my mangled body laying in the street.

Surprisingly, I made it five blocks and not a single car had passed. That was odd considering it was the middle of the afternoon on a sunny Saturday. At the eighth block, my patience started to wane. I stepped down from the curb and walked in the street for a few minutes. Still no cars. I got angrier with every step. God was doing me wrong again.

"You're stopping the cars so I can't die?" I sighed to the single cloud.

The bookstore was only ten minutes away at this point and I had twenty minutes before I needed to clock in. Frustrated, I sat on the curb to wait for my weapon. Still nothing. With eight minutes to make a ten-minute walk I was forced to pick up the pace. I scurried along, glancing behind me every few seconds. When the bookstore came into view, I felt the tears form in my eyes. I walked twelve blocks to work without a single car coming down the busiest street in town on a beautiful, sunny Saturday afternoon. It was ridiculous and it didn't go unnoticed by me. Not only was God allowing my pain, but he refused to let me end it.

So, the pain became part of me. It was me. I didn't know who I was without it. Working with the teens at New Jubilee Fellowship helped me use the pain for good. Ministry gave my pain meaning. I rocked my thorn with sufficient grace until the day Bishop Gilliam, a man I loved and trusted, used the word of God the way Satan used it in Luke 4. That was the blow that broke my spiritual back and left me paralyzed.

I made it through that meeting like a champion, but the aftermath was too much for me to endure. Remember when Elijah called down fire from heaven and then ran off to hide in a cave. It was like that. Three days after the meeting I once again decided that I had enough of God's plan for my life. This time, I wasn't a broken, confused teenager. I knew exactly what I was doing. I knew some people would be devastated but I also knew I couldn't take another step with that ball of agony inside of me.

I weep every time I think about the goodness of God for saving my life. I thank God for the men and women who ran around that room refusing to let me die. Remember the nurse who called on Jesus? As I felt myself fading away, she got in my face with grit teeth. She spoke with such force that droplets of saliva landed on my cheeks.

"Don't you quit on me!" she shouted. The nurse thrust her finger in my face. My vision was so distorted it looked like two fingers, but I could tell by her resolve it was one single, intentional pointer.

That's when the moment shifted. I fought to keep my eyes open while the heaviness of my lids comforted me like a weighted blanket. I couldn't do it. I had to close my eyes. That's when I saw myself as a little girl again. I saw myself standing in the parking lot at New Jubilee Fellowship shouting Psalms 118:17. "I will not die but live and proclaim what the Lord has done." I saw the congregation cheer. I saw news trucks and camera men. Then, I saw Gabe in the back of the crowd, crying the way he did that day at the restaurant.

It wasn't a memory. It was a vision. In fact, it was the harvest of scripture and bible reading that had been planted in me over the years. It was the sermons of all of the preachers I had heard, even Bishop Gilliam, that sprouted in my spirit. Some planted. Some watered. In the moment at the edge of life, God provided an increase. I felt something growing inside of me. It was hope.

The doctor with one blue eye shouted, "One more CC."

Hours later, I woke up in a room full of flowers with one blue eye and one brown eye looking down at me. The doctor flashed a mouthful of whiskey-stained teeth. Teeth and eyes. And flowers. That's what I remember. The nurse who loved Jesus patted my arm with a nod.

The doctor flashed a light in my eyes and held his finger in front of me. There was only one. "You gave us quite a scare young lady."

"I'm sorry," I whimpered.

"You don't owe me any apologies," the doctor said.

The nurse interjected, "She's not talking to you."

She was right. I wasn't talking to the doctor. I was apologizing to God. I was sorry. I was ashamed. I was grateful.

That day, the Wednesday after the New Jubilee meeting, was not the last day I felt overwhelmed by my emotional pain. It was the last day I wanted to die. Life can present you with such pain that you feel like the only relief is death. Let me tell you something…you have the grace to live through those moments. God's grace is sufficient, most sufficient, in those moments.

If you hang out with the spirit of suicide, I pray you find a new companion. Thoughts of suicide are illusions that depict you as weak and inconsequential. You forget about those who love you. You forget about God who has a plan for you. It's a good plan, too.

Suicidal thoughts link you to the past or fixate on your present situation. Sneaky little things, they hide the hope of the future. They lie to you, deceive you, and keep you from seeing the true light of who you are. More importantly, they bury the truth of who God is and what he can do in your situation.

Was my life all roses and rainbows after that? Hardly. After those brave men and women saved my life, I wanted to live every day on purpose. I had a vision for my life that included gray hair and sagging skin. I saw myself as a grandmother and great-grandmother modeled after my own. I developed a hope to become a wise elder who would help guide young women in marriage, work, and life. I developed a strong will to live. That's when I almost died.

It was three weeks before my wedding. I was doing two-a-days on the treadmill to look fabulous on the big day. Since I have a tendency to overdo everything, I pulled a muscle in the back of my knee. At least that's what I thought. I was in so much pain that I climbed the stairs to my bedroom on my hands and knees. That's when I knew I needed help.

When I arrived at the hospital, they found a blood clot in my leg that was five centimeters long. I was a nonsmoker and looked to be in great shape, so they were pretty sure it was an anomaly. My doctor ordered a battery of tests. I was told that it was just a "formality." I'll never forget the look on my doctor's face when he entered the room.

Dr. Hart was an excellent doctor, the best— which is why he ordered all those tests despite me being a young, healthy, non-smoker. He came highly recommended to me with one caveat. "His people skills suck," they all said. They were right.

When Dr. Hart came into the room that day, I immediately knew something was wrong. He was normally a vibrant, caramel color, but that day he looked like a cup of hot cocoa that had been sitting out all day, cold and ashy.

"You're going to die," he said. Yep. Just like that.

I chuckled nervously. "Well, you could have at least warned me that you had bad news."

Dr. Hart went on to explain my condition. He said my lungs were filled with blood clots and there was a large clot at the base of my heart. "If it moves, it's going to kill you."

"I'm not going to die. So, what do you we need to do?" I asked.

"We'll do our best but get your affairs in order," Dr. Hart answered.

I couldn't believe it. His eyes were glossy. Dr. Hart had a heart somewhere deep inside that arsenal of clinical genius. With a big swallow, he turned and walked out of the room.

Once the room cleared of nurses and techs, I looked up at God. "I know you did not save my life to let me go out like this."

Mama, who would normally run point on spiritual matters, was not in the mood to lead. While the church ladies prayed over me, Mama paced around the hospital room with her face shifting from mad to sad and back to mad again. While mama had made the eight-hour drive overnight, my dad peppered the nurse's station with phone calls. By ten minutes after every hour, a nurse would enter and say, "Your father called again."

Taking heed to Dr. Hart's direction, we called in my lawyer to draw up a trust for Caden…just in case. When I signed the papers, it was the first time I stared down my mortality as an opponent. The irony wasn't missed on me. The girl who once wanted nothing more but to die was now facing death with a desire to live. I didn't know whether to shout, "Won't He do it!" because I had the will to live or "Hallelujah" because God finally answered the prayers of my youth. In either case, I knew God was good…all the damn time.

On day three, Dr. Hart declared, "We know how this is going to end folks."

My mother jumped up from her seat. I thought she was going to sock Dr. Hart in his forehead since he had been "speaking death" and getting on her nerves for days. Instead, she threw her head back and shook her fist at the ceiling. "If you let my daughter die, I'll never preach another word for you."

"I'm done with you." Lenox looked to God and declared war.

What the hell?!! Everybody was losing it, mainly because Dr. Hart couldn't have been more dreadful without a black hoodie and a sickle.

I slowly, carefully pushed myself up in the bed. I wasn't supposed to move. I had long since learned not to put God to the test, but this madness needed to be addressed. I frowned at my mother. I cut my eyes at Lenox. I snarled at the three wailing women from the church in the corner whose prayers had gone from bold to brittle.

I felt like Jesus in the Garden of Gethsemane when he came back to sleeping disciples. These Christians couldn't even hold it together for three days before giving up on God. I was heated and I'm sure the influx of emotion wasn't good for me.

"Let me tell y'all something. God is God. He is God today and if I die tonight, he is still going to be God tomorrow." I slid back down to the resting position, struggling to breath. "Y'all tripping."

Suddenly a booming voice banged through the door. "Amen!"

It was Daddy. Remember I told you that I only know of being in same room with both of my parents twice in my life? The day I was born— which I don't actually remember, and another awkward moment. This was that moment. Daddy walked into the hospital room with a Billy Dee kind of calm. I gasped at the sight of Daddy. So did Mama.

My mother had not seen him in over twenty years. I had never seen them in the same lens. There are no pictures of them. They didn't interact. They don't speak about each other. It's as if they never knew each other. The sight was overwhelming. I took a deep sniff from my oxygen tube. I just knew I was going to die. I was wrong.

After nine days, pumped full of blood thinners and pain medication, I walked out of my hospital room to amazed faces and the thunder of applause.

Everybody's life is fragile, but mine seemed to be hanging by a piece of dental floss for many years. Death loomed from the blaze of that house fire to the heat of having seven blood clots in my lungs. I've been wounded and exploited I've been victimized and vilified. I bludgeoned myself with bad decisions and choices that choked my destiny.

Oh, I've certainly had my share of victories. My life has been charted with exceptional highs that match the extraordinary lows of this story. In all of it, God was with me. Whether my life was threatened by men, malady, or my own despair, God saved my life. I did not die but lived to tell everybody what God has done.

***

There are people who are trained to help you overcome suicidal thoughts. If you struggle with feeling like life will be better when it is over, please seek help.

Call the National Suicide Prevention Lifeline at 800-273-8255.

EPILOGUE

My friend Rhea has five sons. She's living the life I wanted and she's doing a way better job at it than I ever could have done. She has a thriving career, and enviable marriage, and manages to look like she belongs on the cover of Essence Magazine while maintaining it all. She was graced for that life. I wasn't. That is God's plan for her life, not mine.

Three weeks after I got out of the hospital, I married Lenox. Three months after that, I found out that I was pregnant. Three weeks after that I miscarried. Two months after that I was pregnant again. Four months after that, I miscarried at the beginning of my second trimester. And yes, six months later I lost another baby. Life didn't get easier after I walked out of that hospital, but my ability to deal with life grew stronger as I deepened my relationship with that fella I met in the snowstorm. His name is Jesus.

When I look back on my life, being a mother was such an important goal for me because I felt like I had been robbed of it by the abuse of my childhood. They broke my body. My struggle with carrying children was a constant reminder of the things that had been done to me. Through those struggles I learned to accept God's will for my life.

I fought against the feelings that Sasha had in her struggles to get pregnant. I actively eliminated thoughts that I didn't deserve to be a mother. I read about mothers in the Bible, like Hannah and Rizpah. I embraced my life and accepted what motherhood would be for me, a painful experience controlled by Marcos. I threw myself into work and began my climb to the top of the world.

After a weeklong business trip, I was so ready to be home with Lenox. As I walked through the airport to my gate, we talked on phone and decided we'd go for dinner and drinks as soon as I landed. I cut our call short because I had to tinkle. I got to the gate and called him back. Before boarding I had to tinkle again. Then on the plane I rocked back and forth waiting for the seatbelt light to disappear. When it did, I ran up the aisle to the bathroom like I had not emptied my bladder in three days. I had been pregnant four times before, I knew what it felt like. That's when I discovered I was pregnant with Aiden. God did it…again.

Aiden, my bright, sweet, kind, powerfully inspiring younger son is the embodiment of the grace and joy this story brings. I guess he's kind of a trophy for me… for all of us, Lenox and Caden, too. When we look at him, we see the goodness of God. When I hear him in uproarious laughter from his bedroom, I know that God fulfilled my vision of what I believe childhood should be and what kind of mother I wanted to be for my children. Life for Caden and I was no crystal stair, but Aiden walks on flowery beds of ease because of our struggles.

Aiden was raised by Lenox and me in one home, the same home from the day he was born. He was raised in the kind of loving, stable home I wanted for myself when I was child. With stability that most people can only dream of, he once astutely described his life as "unicorns and rainbows" acknowledging that he has been blessed. When he was eleven, Aiden gave his life to Christ. Thanks be to God!

Caden has grown up to be all that I had hoped. God answered every prayer. Every one! It turns out, I didn't need to be right there with him every day. I only needed to do what God asked of me. My job was to love Caden relentlessly and let him know that the love of a mother is not affected by time, distance, or petty differences.

I hope my story with Caden encourages other mothers who are separated from their children, no matter the circumstance. If God blessed you to be a mother, seek his wisdom on how he wants you to fulfill the assignment. He will grace you for the journey. I have experienced this grace as both a mother and a child. Caden gave his life to Christ in college. Thanks be to God!

Without a doubt, Caden and Aiden are the illustration of my tumultuous and triumphant relationship with God. They are miracles and answered prayers. Being "mama" helped me better understand my relationship with God. I want to give my sons everything they desire, but I don't. I know giving them everything will stunt their growth. I want to protect them from broken hearts and hurt feelings. I can't. I know that a wounded heart seeks God's comfort.

Being a mother the way I've had to be a mother allowed me to better understand God's way with me. I love my children no matter what they do. There is nothing that will make me stop loving them. This reality helped me understand God's grace and his love for me. The love I have for my children, comes from God. Pay attention to the love inside of you. That's God!

God has certainly been disappointed in some of the decisions I've made, but he has never stopped loving me. He never will. God loves you. He loved you when bad things happened to you. He loved you when you did bad things to yourself. God has forgiven every bad decision and every terrible thought. You owe it to God and to yourself, to forgive yourself of these things. Release shame. Get rid of guilt. Make use of the grace God has given you. When you trust God to walk the path he has chosen for you, even the most egregious things in your story can be used for good.

My life continues to have ups and downs. The pain hasn't totally disappeared. The memories of my past have not vanished, not in the least detail. I communicate with my parents almost daily. They overwhelm me with love and support and guidance. When Daddy hugs me, I still want to cry because I'm grateful. When Mama and I laugh to tears, I give God a quick glimpse of gratitude.

Lenox and I are riding a wave of God's peace and strength. The joy and intimacy we've found in marriage is something I could have never imagined. I feel so undeserving of this life God has given me. That unworthy feeling is where I find His grace.

I don't deserve this life. That's grace. Grace is getting something wonderful you don't deserve. I surely appreciate the mercy of God for sparing me from the consequences of my mistakes and sins. However, in this stage of life, I have been overwhelmed by God's grace.

Writing this book allowed me to see God's grace in retrospect. From this point forward, I'm determined to recognize the grace of God in the moment that it shows up.

***

I have had hundreds of experiences that aren't included in this story. My victories have been astonishing, but I didn't learn much from those. We can see more from the mountain top, but we're often too high to see things clearly. From my experience, it is the low points of life that make us stronger. That is, if we embrace them. Don't rush through the pain. Don't try to side-step the trials.

The moral of this story is simple. Trust God to guide you and use His grace to get through it all. Remain in his grace.

Love Always,

Toyi Elizabeth

READER & BOOK CLUB RESOURCES

PERSONAL JOURNALING EXERCISES

Journaling can often take the form of letters or narratives that we may never share with others but crafting the words brings healing. Toyi Elizabeth used personal journaling as a means to discover her identity and chart her path to healing. Using the book as a guide, begin your own healing journal.

CHAPTER ONE: YOUR STORY

Toyi Elizabeth's earliest memories were the traumatic seeds from which her life grew. What are your earliest memories and how have they shaped your life choices? Write about how these memories have developed your identity, personality, and mindset.

CHAPTER TWO: APOLOGIZE

The death of Nang made Toyi Elizabeth more aware of the need to resolve conflicts and disagreements before it's too late. Who do you need to apologize to? Write an apology letter and discuss how it feels to admit your mistakes.

CHAPTER THREE: YOUR FAITH

Toyi Elizabeth's journey to authentic faith began with an epiphany in a snowstorm. She realized her faith was shallow and powerless. What do you believe about God? Write about your faith. Include the reasons why you believe or don't believe in God. Be specific.

CHAPTER FOUR: FORGIVENESS

Toyi Elizabeth's relationship with her parents was complicated and fostered her ability to forgive people who caused her pain. Who do you need to forgive? Write a letter of forgiveness to someone who hurt you. Make a declaration of how you will move forward.

CHAPTER FIVE: BONDING WITH OTHERS

Toyi Elizabeth and Mama found a common bond in Christ Jesus. They rebuilt their relationship from that central place of understanding. Keeping in mind that the definition of "family" is personal to you, what connects you to your "family"? Write about your family bonds, about shared values, and family experiences that bring you joy.

CHAPTER SIX: COMPASSION

Bobby Sparks is an important figure in the story. Through reflection, Toyi Elizabeth was able to see his brokenness and understand why he caused her so much pain. How can you better understand the people who have hurt you? Consider the pain of those who caused you pain and write about this new perspective to find healing and forgiveness.

CHAPTER SEVEN: FAMILY

Toyi Elizabeth discovered that family is like Noah's Ark, a stinky place for safety and support. What challenges have you overcome in relationships with friends and family? Write about resolved conflicts and express your gratitude for "family".

CHAPTER EIGHT: FRIENDSHIP

Toyi Elizabeth defines friendship as a "journey to unconditional love" where sometimes things get messy. How do you define friendship? Write about your inner circle and how it makes you feel to have good friends, or how it feels to lack genuine friendships.

CHAPTER NINE: LOSS

Toyi Elizabeth is a story of being lifted from loss. Twice, she experienced the sudden loss of a loved one that made finding closure difficult. Where do you still need closure in your life? Write about a loss or situation that remains open in your heart.

CHAPTER TEN: EXPECTATIONS

For many years, Toyi Elizabeth had a "list" that dictated her expectations in personal relationships. What expectations do you have of others that never seem to be met? Write about your expectations and what changes you may need to make to find peace in your relationships.

CHAPTER ELEVEN: BETTER CHOICES

Toyi Elizabeth and Marcos had a toxic, relationship that took years to produce healing and forgiveness. How have toxic relationships affected your life? Write about how you made better choices (or will make better choices) after that experience.

CHAPTER TWELVE: CHURCH

As a Christian, Toyi Elizabeth always went to church somewhere. While it wasn't always positive, she maintained her relationship with the church as a whole. How do you feel about church and church people? Write about your feelings and consider how they may affect your relationship with God.

CHAPTER THIRTEEN: LESSONS LEARNED

Toyi Elizabeth learned a lot from her pain and disappointments. What lessons have you learned from the low points in life? Write about the way you've grown through adversity.

CHAPTER FOURTEEN: DESIRE

Toyi Elizabeth made the life-long mistake of putting people on pedestals, including Bishop Gilliam, to earn love. What do you use to make yourself feel better? Write about the people and things that give you comfort. Consider if those are the healthiest ways for you to achieve healing.

CHAPTER FIFTEEN: GRACE

Toyi Elizabeth discovered that God's grace was the sustaining element of her life. What parts of your story can you solely attribute to God? Write about the ways God has loved you and protected you.

GROUP DISCUSSION QUESTIONS

1. What words would you use to describe Toyi Elizabeth? How did your perspective of her change throughout the story?

2. How would you describe her storytelling? Did you find her to be self-preserving, always painting herself in a good light?

3. What parts of the story made you laugh?

4. What parts of the story made you want to cry?

5. Toyi Elizabeth believes that everyone has an excuse for the pain they've caused and the pain they've felt. Who are the victims and villains in this story? Why do you define them as such?

6. How would you describe Toyi Elizabeth's relationships with her parents? How do you think that affected the way she told the story?

7. When you consider Toyi Elizabeth's relationship with Marcos, who was at fault? Why?

8. How did Toyi Elizabeth finally let go of her expectations in relationships? How do you think this helped or hurt her?

9. How would you describe Toyi Elizabeth's view of friendship? How does it differ from your own?

10. What was Toyi Elizabeth's take on family? What can you learn from her family story?

11. Who was Gabe in Chapter 13? What was his purpose in the story of Toyi Elizabeth? How did she change after that encounter?

12. After all she had survived, why do you think the meeting at New Jubilee drove Toyi Elizabeth to suicide?

13. How would you describe the significance of Toyi Elizabeth's faith in God? How is it related to her relationship with the church?

14. What part of Toyi Elizabeth's story gives you the most hope?

15. What parts of the story are missing? What more would you like to know about Toyi Elizabeth and her story?

PRAYERS FROM THE AUTHOR

My purpose for writing this book is not only to entertain you with an engaging story. It is also to bring healing, restoration, and reconciliation into your life through art. Prayer and Bible study are a very important part of my life. Together, I have found them to be survival tools to help better understand who God is and who you are.

We have included prayers for the key themes of this story. Pray these prayers as often as you need to pray them. God is listening.

Pray to Accept Your Story

Dear God, thank you for creating me for a purpose. Let me live out your vision for my life. Continue to reveal who I am and give me the wisdom to accept it. Change me daily to be more like you want me to be. Transform me by renewing my mind on this journey with you. In the name of the Lord Jesus, I pray. Amen.

Pray to Learn to Apologize

Dear Lord, thank you for helping me recognize my mistakes and for giving me a heart that feels bad about it. Please give me the courage to apologize to those I have wronged. Show me who I need to apologize to and guide me in how to do it. Give me the words. Provide the opportunity. Lord, let my apology be received with grace. Amen.

Pray to Learn to Forgive

God, give me a clean heart and renew a right spirit in me. Give me a forgiving heart towards those who have wronged me. Help me to see them the way you see them. Remove all bitterness and malice from me. Give me the grace to forgive. In the mighty name of Jesus, I pray. Amen.

Pray to Face Your Problems

Lord, you can do anything. Nothing is impossible with you. Lord, give me the strength and courage to face the situations in my life. Fill my heart with love and truth. Guide me through this so that I live your perfect will for me. I can face this situation because I know you are with me. So, thank you for being here. Amen.

Pray to Accept Your Healing

Dear God, thank you for the good plans you have for me. Help me to get beyond my past and give me hope for the future. Heal my heart and mind so that I can move forward and grow deeper in your love. Bring reconciliation, restoration, and recovery into my life...in the name of Jesus. Amen.

Pray to Get to Know Jesus Better

Dear Lord, thank you for forgiving me of my sins. I know who you are Jesus, but I want to know you better. Come into my heart and guide me every day. Give me eyes to see you. Give me ears to hear you. Give me a heart to know you and obey you. Thank you for loving me. I pray this prayer in your name. Amen.

ABOUT THE AUTHOR

Kamryn Adams started writing in wide-ruled, wire-bound notebooks as a young girl and continued to privately create stories through her adolescence. In college, she wrote a short story called "The Pink Bow" about a young girl raised in an abusive home. The paper caught the attention of her English professor who encouraged her to maintain a life-long love of writing. Though her stories are not autobiographical, she writes with an authenticity that connects readers to healing and inspiration for their own lives. She loves reading, writing, dancing and gardening. She also has a serious addiction to word games. A self-proclaimed "Bible Nerd", Kamryn writes to inspire audiences to love God, themselves, and others.

CONNECT WITH KAMRYN ADAMS

To book Kamryn for your book club or event go to:
www.KamrynAdams.com
Instagram: @kamrynadams
Facebook: @kamrynadamsofficial

CPSIA information can be obtained
at www.ICGtesting.com
Printed in the USA
BVHW042246011022
648380BV00033B/603/J